ISO 9001:2015

in Plain English

Other Paton Professional Books by Craig Cochran

- *Becoming a Customer-Focused Organization*
- *The Continual Improvement Process*
- *Customer Satisfaction: Tools, Techniques, and Formulas for Success*
- *Internal Auditing in Plain English (Coming Soon)*
- *Problem Solving in Plain English*
- *The 7 Lessons: Management Tools for Success*

Order these and other titles online at *www.patonprofessional.com.*

ISO 9001:2015

in Plain English

Craig Cochran

Chico, California

Most Paton Professional books are available at quantity discounts when purchased in bulk. For more information, contact:

Paton Professional
PO Box 44
Chico, CA 95927-0044
Telephone: (530) 342-5480
Email: books@patonprofessional.com
Web: www.patonprofessional.com

© 2015 by Craig Cochran. All rights reserved.
Printed in the United States of America

20 19 18 17 16 15   10 9 8 7 6 5 4 3 2 1

ISBN: 978-1-932828-72-6

Library of Congress Cataloging in Publication Data on File

Notice of Rights
No part of this work covered by the copyright herein may be reproduced or used in any form or by any means—graphic, electronic, or mechanical, including photo-copying, recording, taping, or information storage and retrieval systems—without permission in writing from Paton Professional.

Notice of Liability
The information in this book is distributed on an "as is" basis, without warranty. Al-though every precaution has been taken in the preparation of the book, neither the author nor Paton Professional shall have any liability to any person or entity with respect to any loss or damage caused or alleged to be caused directly or indirectly by the information contained in this book.

Staff
Editor & Publisher: Scott M. Paton
Assistant Editors: Daniel Taylor and Laura Smith
Book design: Anita Jovanovic
Cover design: Miguel Kilantang

To Muriel, a model of patience and love

Contents

This book is not intended as a replacement for the ISO 9001:2015 standard.
If you haven't read the standard, do so—now!
It's also a good idea to read ISO 9000:2015, which is the normative
reference for ISO 9001:2015.
You can buy them both at *www.iso.org* or
your country's national standards body.

Chapter 1

Introduction

ISO 9001 might be the most confusing document in business history. I first became aware of the standard in the late 1980s when my manager handed it to me and said, "See if you can figure this thing out. Our plant has to get certified." I took the document back to my desk and attempted to read it. The first attempt was a failure. On the second attempt, I got a little further. On the third attempt, I think I read the whole thing, but I still wasn't sure what it said. All I could remember was "blah, blah, blah... quality system." And we were supposed to get certified to this? Impossible.

We did get certified, of course. It was the first step in a long relationship with ISO 9001. With every subsequent experience, there were new discoveries and revelations, and it was common to hear employees say that they wished the standard was easier to understand. What lies at heart of all this confusion? The crux of the problem is that ISO 9001 was written to apply to any kind of organization. When you write a document that's applicable to *everyone*, you end up with something that's not very well suited to *anyone*. Another problem is that ISO 9001 was written by committee. There were a lot of hands stirring the pot, so the resulting standard is more complex than it would be had it been the work of a single person.

Before we get too much further, let's rewind with some basics. ISO 9001 is an international quality management system (QMS) standard. It presents fundamental management and quality assurance practices that can be applied by any organization. The requirements represent an excellent foundation of planning, control, and improvement for just about any enterprise. Without a QMS, organizations have little chance of sustaining any improvements or innovations they might realize. I believe that ISO 9001 is a basic model for managing any enterprise. It goes beyond what many people traditionally consider "quality." In fact, I avoid using the word quality in relation to the standard anytime I can get away with it. ISO 9001 is a management system standard, period.

Because it's generic, ISO 9001 is also quite flexible. In few places does it specify exactly what an organization must do. In most cases, the standard leaves a great deal of discretion to the organization in terms of how it will design its processes and procedures. This enables organizations to customize it to ensure individual success, instead of just blindly following a standard. The drawback, of course, is that the organization has to customize its approach to ISO 9001 compliance. I've had more than a few clients tell me, "I just wish ISO 9001 would come out and say exactly what we need to do." Well, that's not the way it works. The organization must figure out the best way to meet the requirements, and this is both liberating and challenging.

"Shall" is the operative word in ISO 9001. This word indicates a requirement wherever it appears. This can take a variety of forms, depending on the specificity of the requirement and the needs of the company. A "shall" can often be satisfied by communicating a requirement, developing a process, documenting a procedure, keeping a record, training personnel, inspecting a product, or any number of other controls. In many cases, ISO 9001 leaves it up to the organization to decide exactly how it will address each requirement. The "shalls" of ISO 9001 start in section 4 and continue through section 10. Materials outside of these sections, such as the introductory text at the beginning of the standard and sections 1–3, are for guidance and illustration purposes only. This material is not auditable, and an organization is not expected to interpret it as requirements.

The present version of ISO 9001—ISO 9001:2015—is the fifth iteration of the standard. Here is a brief history of ISO 9001 through the years:

- *ISO 9001:1987.* The first publication of ISO 9001. Truly a manufacturing standard and very heavily focused on documentation. The requirements were based on U.S. military standards used by government contractors since World War II.

- *ISO 9001:1994.* A minor revision to the standard. Still very prescriptive and focused on manufacturing. Difficult for services providers to interpret and apply.
- *ISO 9001:2000.* A significant revision of the standard with a focus on continual improvement, customer satisfaction, leadership, and process management. An attempt to make the standard more applicable to service providers, and to make it more flexible in general.
- *ISO 9001:2008.* A very minor revision with only slight changes in wording. No actual requirements were added, removed, or changed.
- *ISO 9001:2015:* A significant revision to the standard and another step away from its manufacturing origins. Much more of a model for managing and improving an organization, with risk lying at the heart of the standard. An excellent framework for long-term success and customer satisfaction.

Until ISO 9001:2015, the standard has simply been a set of requirements. Organizations did their best to understand and implement them. The approach was similar to trying on clothes labeled one-size-fits-all. You might get lucky with a good fit, but more likely there would be a number of places where ISO 9001 simply didn't feel right. ISO 9001:2015 is now a risk-based standard. The risks and opportunities that an organization identifies are drawn from each company's unique circumstances. There's nothing one-size-fits-all about this approach. You determine what's most important to your success and build your QMS around these unique issues. The result is a management system that you can truly say is built for your business. Is the identification of risks and opportunities an important step in implementing ISO 9001:2015? Yes, possibly the most important step.

Planning is another key theme of ISO 9001:2015. This theme is embodied through a number of different sections and clauses in the standard. Clause 4.1 asks you to examine the internal and external issues that are key to your success. ISO 9001:2015 refers to these as the context of the organization. This is fundamental environmental scanning intended to answer the question, "Who are we and what does our competitive environment look like?" This is followed by clause 4.2, which asks you to identify your interested parties. You not only identify these entities, but you also attempt to determine what their needs and expectations are. Clauses 4.1 and 4.2 constitute the raw material that is fed into your process for determining risks and opportunities.

ISO 9001:2015 emphasizes change management. Expected change must be carefully and deliberately planned, with all pieces in place ahead of time. For production changes that happen more in real time, the organization is required to evaluate the effect of the changes. These requirements are embodied in two different clauses of the standard: 6.3 and 8.5.6.

Organizational knowledge is an interesting new requirement. It asks the question, "What are we learning from our experiences?" Successful organizations seize every experience, whether good or bad, as an opportunity to build a storehouse of learning and knowledge. They must learn and build their knowledge or they won't survive. ISO 9001:2015 asks you to establish a process for capturing this organizational knowledge. Once you capture it, you must maintain it and make it available to your personnel.

The role of top management has been expanded significantly. ISO 9001:2015 asks top management to demonstrate leadership on a number of important topics. These include taking accountability for the effectiveness of the QMS, promoting the process approach and risk-based thinking, and promoting improvement. These requirements serve to raise the stakes significantly for top management's involvement within the scope of the QMS. The leader of the QMS is no longer a quality manager or quality director. The leader of the QMS is top management.

The concept of the process approach has been strengthened and reinforced. Process management has long been a mainstay of the QMS, but ISO 9001:2015 nudges it a bit further. The standard defines all the various components of a process (such as inputs, outputs, criteria and methods, resources, responsibilities and authorities, risks and opportunities, evaluation, and improvement) and requires that these processes be documented where necessary. Documentation that reflects this way of thinking is inherently simpler and easier to grasp, and it tends to be more inclusive of all the factors of success for each job, activity, or task.

One of the baffling changes within ISO 9001:2015 is the disappearance of the terms "document" and "record." The very concept of a document and a record has been turned on its head, and the standard addresses them as if they're the same. In reality, there are distinct differences between documents and records. Thankfully, ISO 9001:2015 gives us some code words to differentiate the terms. If the standard talks about *maintaining documented information,* it's talking about a document: living information that is subject to change. If the standard talks about *retaining documented information*, it's referring to a record: historical proof of having done something. The difference hinges on *maintaining* vs. *retaining.*

Let's take a quick look at ISO 9001:2015's introduction and ten sections. This will be the only mention of the introduction and sections 1–3, as they are only in the standard for guidance purposes. You don't have to implement them. Sections 4–10 will be covered in much detail in the remainder of the book, as these include the "shalls" (requirements) of the standard.

INTRODUCTION

0.1   *General.* Implementing a management system is a strategic decision, intended to drive the success of the organization. The process approach is a key theme of ISO 9001:2015, as is risk-based thinking.

0.2   *Quality management principles.* Seven principles are at the foundation of ISO 9001:2015: customer focus, leadership, engagement of people, process approach, improvement, evidence-based decision making, and relationship management.

0.3.1 *Process approach—General.* An organization is composed of linked activities—processes that transform inputs to outputs. The requirements of ISO 9001:2015 are organized as processes, with explicit connections from one process to the next.

0.3.2 *Plan-do-check-act cycle.* The plan-do-check-act (PDCA) cycle is an improvement methodology that can be applied to any process.

0.3.3 *Risk-based thinking.* Risk-based thinking has been implicit in previous revisions of ISO 9001, but now it is an explicit requirement in ISO 9001:2015. Actions to address risks and opportunities are key drivers of the QMS.

0.4   *Relationship with other management system standards.* The structure of

ISO 9001:2015 was modified to make it more compatible with other management system standards, such as ISO 14001. ISO 9001:2015 makes use of two guidance documents that are designed to aid users in the interpretation of the standard. These guidance documents are ISO 9000:2015 (*Quality management systems—Fundamentals and vocabulary*) and ISO 9004:2009 (*Managing for the sustained success of an organization*).

1 SCOPE

ISO 9001:2015 is intended to be used by organizations that desire to produce products and services that meet customer and applicable statutory and regulatory requirements, and that wish to enhance customer satisfaction through the use of a QMS. ISO 9001:2015 was written to apply to any organization, no matter what kind of product or services it produces, or what kind of processes it employs.

2 NORMATIVE REFERENCES

ISO 9000:2015, the fundamentals and vocabulary standard, is the normative reference for ISO 9001:2015. In theory, this means that the definitions it provides may be used to clarify and reinforce requirements in ISO 9001:2015.

3 TERMS AND DEFINITIONS

The guidance document ISO 9000:2015 provides the terms to be used in ISO 9001:2015.

4 CONTEXT OF THE ORGANIZATION

This section comprises foundational activities that influence the way the rest of the standard is applied in the organization. These activities include understanding the organization and its context, understanding the needs and expectations of interested parties, and determining the scope of the QMS and its processes. These are not only the first auditable sections of ISO 9001:2015, but they also represent the first sections that an organization would need to implement. A number of subsequent requirements rely on clauses 4.1 and 4.2 as inputs.

5 LEADERSHIP

Top management plays an integral role in ISO 9001:2015, and one could realistically say that the success of the QMS depends on their engagement and leadership. This section includes leadership and commitment; developing and communicating the quality policy; and roles, responsibilities, and authorities. The requirements for management review—another staple of top management involvement—can be found in clause 9.3.

6 PLANNING

This section builds on the requirements defined in section 4, Context of the organization. Much of section 6 uses section 4 as inputs. This section includes such key requirements as actions to address risks and opportunities, quality objectives and planning, and planning of changes.

7 SUPPORT

This section represents key activities that facilitate the core production processes. These requirements encompass resources that must be determined and provided, along with administrative activities. Specific requirements include people, infrastructure, environment for the operation of processes, monitoring and measuring resources (formerly known as calibration), organizational knowledge, competence, awareness, communication, and documented information (also known as document control and record control).

8 OPERATION

This is the longest section of ISO 9001:2015, and it represents the production requirements of the standard. Production, of course, can refer to the manufacturing of a product or the execution of a service. Requirements in section 8 include operational planning and control; requirements for products and services; design and development; control of externally provided processes, products, and services (also known as purchasing); production and service provision; release of products and services; and control of nonconforming outputs.

9 PERFORMANCE EVALUATION

The essence of improvement is an organization's ability to monitor, measure, analyze, and evaluate. This section addresses the processes that drive improvement within an organization, including customer satisfaction, analysis and evaluation, internal audit, and management review. The next section of ISO 9001:2015 is titled "Improvement," but from a practical standpoint, section 9 is where the action is.

10 IMPROVEMENT

The requirements in this final section of ISO 9001:2015 are a fitting capstone for your QMS. They include improvement, nonconformity and corrective action, and continual improvement. Strictly for the sake of continuity, section 10 could have easily been incorporated into section 9. Sections 9 and 10 really flow together as one integrated set of requirements.

Don't be intimidated by ISO 9001:2015. It's a model for success that can be utilized by any organization. The remainder of this book will help you understand how to apply it in the smartest manner possible.

Chapter 2

ISO 9001:2015 Section 4 Context of the Organization

4.1 UNDERSTANDING THE ORGANIZATION AND ITS CONTEXT

No equivalent requirements in ISO 9001:2008. Completely new.

This clause could be titled "Take a hard look around you." That's exactly what the requirement is asking you to do, and it's a logical starting point for ISO 9001:2015. The organization must explore the major elements of its internal and external environment, being as objective and honest as possible, no matter what's revealed. You'd think that most organizations would already be doing this, but most companies are so busy just surviving on a daily basis that this kind of self-reflection is a luxury. Yes, an organization can't be successful in the long term without this kind of examination. An organization can tread water, though, and that's exactly what many do.

Attempting to understand the organization and its context is quite difficult to do in a fresh and unbiased way. Organizational members are already walking around with their eyes open, looking at the issues that face them on a daily basis. They are looking, but are they really *seeing*? To truly comprehend the organization and its context, it's helpful to ask some questions that force managers to alter their perspectives. Questions like:

- What are we especially good at?
- What do our competitors fear about us?
- What helps us close sales with new customers?
- What aspects of our organizational culture are especially helpful to us?
- What could put us out of business if we're not careful?
- What really bothers our customers about us?
- What does everyone agree we need to improve?
- What do newcomers to our organization think we need to improve?
- What new products or services are our customers asking for?
- What weaknesses do our competitors have that we can exploit?
- What emerging technologies could assist us?
- What unmet needs in the marketplace can we take advantage of?
- Where are our costs increasing the fastest?
- What is our biggest category of customer complaints?
- What legal or regulatory issues have the potential to cripple us?
- Where do we need more knowledge and training?

These questions loosely follow the pattern of a strengths-weaknesses-opportunities-threats (SWOT) analysis. ISO 9001:2015 doesn't require organizations to use this method, but it provides a useful and well-balanced model. Thinking about this requirement through the SWOT construct highlights that what ISO 9001:2015 is asking for is actually strategic planning. More accurately, it's the environmental scanning phase of strategic planning. This broadens the scope of ISO 9001:2015 significantly. Instead of just being about traditional "quality" topics, the standard is asking for a holistic analysis of the organization and its environment. Anything is fair game here: finance, safety, security, regulatory—whatever matters to the organization.

This broader perspective could be uncomfortable to those who are accustomed to taking a narrow approach to quality. This isn't quality with a lower-case "q." It is QUALITY in all caps, reflecting on everything the organization does. The self-reflection and environmental scanning required by clause 4.1 should be broad and inclusive. All topics bearing on the organization's success can and should be considered.

Involve people with unique perspectives who are outside the core group when answering these questions. Some of the most valuable participants are new employees. They haven't been corrupted by groupthink and generally have an unvarnished view of operations.

Controversial topics could arise during the analysis required by clause 4.1. In fact, this is desirable. A true analysis of the organization and its environment is going to touch on subjects that make people uncomfortable. Given this reality, it's important that the analysis be led by a facilitator. The facilitator will manage the group dynamics, keep everyone on task, and ensure that any conflict is focused on ideas and not personalities. Another important role of a facilitator is to make sure that nobody dominates the analysis. Top management occasionally has a habit of "having all the answers." This isn't the time for old answers. A fresh examination is the aim, and the facilitator will keep anybody from hijacking the discussions.

ISO 9001:2015 doesn't mention documenting the results of this activity. Conceivably, an organization could meet the requirements of ISO 9001:2015 without it. This isn't very practical, though. Undocumented information is difficult to communicate, monitor, review, or revise. It basically becomes "tribal knowledge," and a topic like this is far too important to be tribal knowledge. Bottom line: Document the results of your external and internal analysis. If your organization arrives at a particularly effective process for performing this, you might also want to document the procedure.

ISO 9001:2015 requires that the information from this process be monitored and reviewed. This suggests two separate, but related, activities. First, the information is monitored. In a practical sense, this requires that management compare actual events against the information that resulted from the examination of the internal and external environment. How much of a difference is there? Is the world changing in ways we didn't expect? Are we becoming a different organization than we thought we were? The monitoring could result in revisions to what we initially determined.

The term "reviewed" suggests a more formal revisiting of the information. It could happen during management review, or through another process. In either case, the organization would maintain records of the review, including who was involved and what was decided. The review may serve as a confirmation that circumstances haven't changed, or it may trigger a full re-examination of the internal and external environment. The key distinction between monitoring and review is that monitoring suggests a formal process that takes place continually; review suggests a more structured, periodic event.

ISO 9001:2015 doesn't state a frequency for re-examining the external and internal environment. The question that should be answered related to frequency is, "How often do things change around here?" We live in a world of turbulence and unpredictability, and the competitive environment can change in a matter of days. It's reasonable to say that external and internal analysis should happen at least once a year. Some organizations may opt to do it even more often, based on what they learn from monitoring and review of the process.

There are two notes at the end of this clause. The first note says that the external analysis should include a wide range of factors bearing on the organization's success, including emerging technologies, the legal environment, actions of competitors, and society in general. It also says that these issues could originate from any geographical source, near or far. The second note delivers the same message, but it focuses on the internal examination. Issues include what people believe, the values they bring to work, the culture of the organization, and other factors. Translation: Cast a wide net when doing your examination. Consider everything that could affect you in the environment. This isn't a minor exercise. It's a significant process that establishes a foundation for the entire management system.

In summary:

- Examine the external and internal environments.
- Do it honestly and with a fresh perspective.
- Document what you learn and use it as an input to the rest of your management system. Note: Documenting this is not a requirement of ISO 9001:2015, though it would make the process sustainable and easier to communicate.
- Monitor and review the information, and periodically go through the whole process again.

Here's an example of how this analysis might look for a fictitious organization:

Company Name: ACME Powder Coating & Painting Inc.

Strengths:

- Experience in the industry
- Willingness to constantly adapt and grow the business
- Capabilities in every coating industry: powders, liquids, fusion-bonded, thermoplastics, marine coatings, chemical warfare coatings, high-corrosive coating, conductive and nonconductive coatings
- Ability to meet tight tolerances (percentage of gloss, mil thickness)
- Background in pretreatments (alkaline degreasers, shot blast, conversion coatings such as iron phosphate and chromium phosphate)
- Ability to invest in new equipment; possess liquid assets
- Less red tape in a small town

Weaknesses:

- Location not on major industrial corridor
- Finding qualified employees
- Labor-intensive coating facility; very limited automation
- Large-volume jobs have eluded our attention; we have missed a lot of opportunities
- Lack of space in current facility
- Growth opportunity in current facility is limited
- Outsourced services (such as IT) are limited in our town and aren't very responsive
- Perception among some customers that our location is too far away to send their work

Opportunities:

- With weak economy, many competitors are going out of business
- Ability to seize the opportunities from other companies' poor-quality work
- New facility on I-75 corridor, more accessible to industrial customers
- Have discussed partnership with two investors

Threats:

- Many companies outsource their coatings to overseas providers
- Many companies are investing in their own small coating lines, instead of using outside providers
- Growth of environmental regulations
- Governmental and municipal customers choosing suppliers on the basis of price alone
- Low-cost providers doing poor work, destroying the industry, and motivating low opinions of powder coating
- Competitors who are getting desperate and under-bidding jobs
- Growing theft in the current business park
- Our county is not very business friendly

4.1 FREQUENTLY ASKED QUESTIONS

Does top management have to be involved with understanding the organization and its context?

ISO 9001:2015 doesn't stipulate who has to be involved. However, it makes sense to involve top managers, because they usually have a very good grasp of global issues that other employees lack. Also, involving top management helps to reinforce the significance of this important planning activity.

4.2 UNDERSTANDING THE NEEDS AND EXPECTATIONS OF INTERESTED PARTIES

No equivalent requirements in ISO 9001:2008. Completely new.

The short description for this clause could read, "Who cares about your organization, and what do they want from you?" Quite literally, those are the questions you're being asked to answer. ISO 9001:2015 uses the term "interested parties." This rather vague term begs the question, "What's an interested party?" It's anyone who has an interest in your operation, no matter whether official business is transacted or not. Interested parties are any people or entities that believe they affect, are affected, or could be affected by your organization. This is a very broad definition, so it will require some true examination to take an inventory of all the interested parties.

Interested parties can occupy a wide spectrum of entities. These are some of the most common, along with a few less common ones:

- *Customers.* Undoubtedly the most important interested party, customers are the reason for your existence. The needs and expectations of customers should drive the majority of the processes within your organization.

- *Suppliers.* Providing you with raw materials, supplies, spare parts, and services, suppliers insert value throughout your supply chain, usually filling in gaps that are too complex, expensive, or distracting to fill yourself.

- *Employees.* These are your team members. Like any team, the players require some sort of compensation, information about team direction, and feedback on performance. Employees also expect some degree of stability and security.

- *Owners.* All business organizations have owners of some sort. Sole proprietors, partners, and shareholders all expect the organization to produce a reasonable rate of return for their investment and associated risk.

- *Community.* The area of homes, businesses, and other entities surrounding the organization could be called its community. The community desires a responsible company that attempts to work with its neighbors, not against them.

- *Schools and colleges.* The primary role of schools and colleges is to impart knowledge and build skills. One of the best measures of this is employability. Schools should know what competencies are required by your organization, so they can be a supplier of human capital.

- *Regulatory bodies.* Compliance is the product that regulators want. Clean air, water, and soil; responsible waste disposal; and ethical employee behavior represent examples of these products.

- *Law enforcement.* Employees and managers are all expected to act within the law. Legal issues include theft, breach of contract, violence, and many others. The repercussions of legal problems are often personal, but these directly affect the organization.

- *Emergency responders.* Firefighters and paramedics respond to reports of emergencies. They want to know about toxic chemicals, flammable substances, and other variables so they can be more effective and not expose their own personnel to undue hazards.
- *News media.* Honesty and transparency are outcomes that news media desire. Interaction with news media varies drastically depending on the size and nature of the organization.

Not all of these interested parties are applicable to every organization. Your job is to identify which ones do apply. The next step is to identify the requirements of the interested parties that relate to your QMS. Figure 2.1 shows some examples of interested parties, along with their requirements.

Figure 2.1	Examples of Interested Parties	
Interested party	**Requirements**	**QMS processes**
Customers	• Orders accurately taken • Products arrive on time • All product specifications met	• Sales and customer service process • Shipping and logistics process • Inspection process
Suppliers	• Accurate purchase orders • Timely payment of invoices*	• Purchasing process • Accounts payable process*
Employees	• Clear instructions and training • Paychecks accurate and on time* • Resolution of grievances*	• Training process • Payroll process* • Human resources process*
Managers	• Current information for decision making	• Management review process • Reporting on quality objectives
Owners	• Receive favorable return on investment*	• Finance process*

Figure 2.1	Examples of Interested Parties	
Interested party	Requirements	QMS processes
Community	• No excessive truck traffic*	• Shipping and logistics process
Schools and colleges	• Consideration of graduates as employees*	• Recruiting and hiring process* • Training process
Regulatory bodies	• Regulatory compliance*	• Listing of applicable regulations* • Regulatory compliance process*
Law enforcement	• Compliance with all laws • Reporting of illegal activities*	• Human resources process*
Emergency responders	• Reporting of dangerous substances* • Planned approach to emergencies*	• Emergency response process* • Emergency maps and contact lists*
News media	• Response to requests for information*	• Public relations process*

The great majority of QMS processes are designed to address one particular interested party: customers. ISO 9001:2015 asks you to think beyond this obvious interested party and consider others that could affect your success. Quite a few of the requirements shown in figure 2.1 aren't typically addressed within the QMS, and these are indicated by asterisks. Does this mean that you're required to drastically broaden your QMS to address them? No, of course not, but you should consider these requirements and determine how they could affect your system. It's possible that after some consideration, you and your team may decide to add a process or two to your QMS simply because of how important the interested party is to your success. After creating your own list of interested parties and requirements, ask the following simple questions to decide how relevant the interested parties are:

- Could the interested party stop our operations?
- Could the interested party alter our process or product?
- Do we rely on the interested party for our long-term success?

If the answer is yes to any of these questions, then it's quite possible that the interested party is relevant to your QMS. In these cases, it might be worth broadening the QMS to address the interested party and its requirements. Ultimately, the decision lies solely with your organization. ISO 9001:2015 is simply asking you to consider interested parties with a fresh set of eyes.

In summary:

- Make a list of all the interested parties related to your organization.
- Briefly determine the requirements of the interested parties.
- Decide if the requirements are relevant to your QMS.
- Document what you learn and use it as an input to the rest of your management system. Note: Documenting this is not a requirement of ISO 9001:2015, though it would make the process sustainable and easier to communicate.
- Monitor and formally review the information regularly.

4.2 FREQUENTLY ASKED QUESTIONS

Where do we draw the line with interested parties? You could go on and on with this.

The key is how much of an impact they have on your organization. Start with the parties who have a significant effect on your ability to provide conforming products, meet customer requirements, and stay within the law. This is going to include customers, suppliers, subcontractors, employees, regulators, local police, and fire departments. Beyond these high-impact entities, it's up to you how far you want to go with interested parties.

4.2 FREQUENTLY ASKED QUESTIONS

How can we possibly determine the expectations of interested parties? We can't read their minds.

You can't read their minds, but you can ask them. For the important categories of interested parties, ask them what they believe to be their needs and expectations, now and in the future. The more dialogue and communication you have with interested parties, the better off your organization will be.

4.3 DETERMINING THE SCOPE OF THE QUALITY MANAGEMENT SYSTEM

Similar to subclause 4.2.2 in ISO 9001:2008, but more expansive in terms of what must be considered.

In past revisions of ISO 9001, the subject of "scope" warranted a single sentence. Notably, ISO 9001:2015 devotes an entire clause of the standard to scope. Has the scope of the QMS suddenly become more important, or did past revisions just not give the topic its due? Actually, scope has always been an important detail, but ISO 9001:2015 makes it even more critical. That's because the preceding two clauses of the standard provide the raw material for the scope. You're expected to make an informed decision about the scope of the QMS based on your understanding of the organization and its context and interested parties.

Before we go any further, let's discuss what scope is. The scope of the QMS is its boundary. This boundary relates to two different entities:

- *The boundary of the QMS in terms of your organization's processes.* In other words, what parts of your company will be included within the QMS? This is written as a scope statement that appears in your documentation.
- *The requirements of ISO 9001:2015 that apply to your organization.* All requirements are intended to apply. The only exception is when a requirement simply doesn't have any relevance to your organization. An example is the design-and-development section of ISO 9001:2015. If

your organization receives complete product/service specifications from your customers, then there is nothing to design. This is documented as an exclusion and justification statement.

So, you see that scope is comprised of two separate statements. From a certification standpoint, the scope is essential because it tells the certification body what parts of your organization are fair game during an audit. It also tells the certification body which requirements of ISO 9001:2015 it should apply to you. Internally, scope is important because it communicates to the organization which departments and processes must adhere to ISO 9001:2015's requirements.

Here is an example of a scope statement as it might appear in a company's documentation:

The scope of the quality management system is the manufacture, inspection, and shipping of thermal insulation bricks. The design-and-development requirements of ISO 9001:2015 have been excluded because the organization does not perform any design of its products or services. All product requirements and specifications are received from customers.

In this example, the processes listed are manufacturing, inspection, and shipping. Support processes such as purchasing and sales aren't mentioned because it's assumed that these activities are taking place to facilitate manufacturing. Also, the subprocesses within manufacturing usually aren't specifically mentioned unless there is a good reason for doing so. The most common reason for listing subprocesses within the scope statement is when the scope has been intentionally limited. Finally, the scope excludes design and development, and it justifies why these requirements don't apply.

One of the major purposes of the work you did in clauses 4.1 and 4.2 was to better understand your organization's processes so you would know what should be within the scope of the QMS. Internal and external issues that affect the success of the organization (as identified in clause 4.1) will benefit from the structure and discipline of ISO 9001:2015. Also, the needs and expectations of interested parties (as identified in clause 4.2) will be better served through processes that are guided by ISO 9001:2015. The standard requires that the organization consider three things when determining the QMS scope:

- The organization's internal and external environment, also known as context (clause 4.1)
- The views of interested parties (clause 4.2)
- Your products and services (clause 4.3)

By exploring and considering these three elements, your organization will make a better decision about what should be included in its QMS. You're more likely to craft a scope that includes the key factors of success for your organization.

Let's examine each one of these inputs individually and discuss how they might be considered within the scope.

Organization and its context

Back in clause 4.1 of ISO 9001:2015, the organization examined its internal and external environment and determined the issues that drive its success. As you may recall, I likened it to a SWOT analysis, where strengths, weaknesses, opportunities, and threats are identified. This exercise, if done correctly, should have revealed a deeper understanding of your organiza-

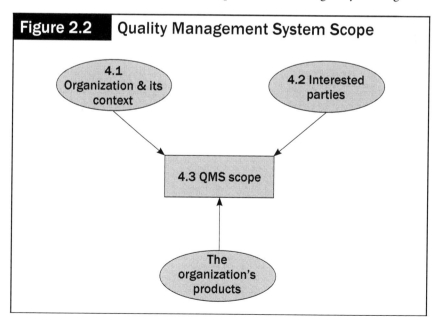

Figure 2.2 Quality Management System Scope

tion. What are we good at? Where are we weak? What are our opportunities? Which risks pose the biggest threats to us? Ideally, you should use your QMS to help manage these issues. At the very least, you're required to consider these issues when determining your QMS scope. How does this happen? One of the best methods would be through a thorough discussion at the highest levels of the organization.

From a practical standpoint, the more broadly a standard is applied, the more likely it is to drive improvement. ISO 9001:2015 should be applied to every department and function within the organization. If it isn't, there will be pockets of "looseness" within the company. Why not just expect all functions to operate in a systematic manner? Anything short of this is an invitation to confusion and chaos. Many people will point out that ISO 9001:2015 is a quality management system, with an emphasis on the word "quality." Quality simply means the ability to meet requirements. Meeting requirements is the job of every process in the organization, which means that a QMS is an excellent model for everybody.

It's still up to the organization to define exactly what the scope of its QMS will be. ISO 9001:2015 addresses the issue of scope mainly through the requirements of the standard, stating that where a requirement can be applied, it should be applied. This means that organizations can't exclude parts of the standard for the sake of convenience. One of the most common sections that companies have often tried to exclude is design and development. The reason? It seemed very prescriptive, and they preferred not to subject their design processes to such rigor. Of course, this isn't allowable. If you are performing any of the functions mentioned in ISO 9001:2015, you have to include them within the scope of the QMS.

4.3 FREQUENTLY ASKED QUESTIONS

Do all of our products and services have to be within the scope of the QMS?

No, your organization determines the QMS scope. That said, the broader the QMS is applied, the more benefit you'll get out of it.

4.3 FREQUENTLY ASKED QUESTIONS

What happened to the requirement for a quality manual?

It no longer exists in ISO 9001:2015. The scope of the QMS must be maintained as documented information (clause 4.3), and you must define the processes necessary for the QMS (clause 4.4), but these are the only remaining vestiges of the requirement. If you see value in a top-level quality manual, then by all means keep it.

4.4 QUALITY MANAGEMENT SYSTEM AND ITS PROCESSES

Equivalent to clause 4.1 in ISO 9001:2008, with more rigor implied.

ISO 9001 has been a process-based standard for a long time. ISO 9001:2015 continues this emphasis with more clarity on the components of a process. You're required to determine the processes needed by your organization and to define a number of key details about them, such as their inputs, outputs, criteria, methods, and measurements. This requires the organization to consider all the various elements of a process, not just the one or two pieces believed to be the most important. The result is an organization that truly knows itself and understands what it takes to be successful.

Is ISO 9001:2015 asking for you to define all your processes this way? That's not completely clear, but it does say "processes needed for the quality management system." It would be wise to brainstorm a list of the major processes within the organization and start on these. There's no need to change your existing documentation, which is probably structured in a traditional text-based format. If your existing documentation works for you, then by all means keep it in place. The process orientation can serve as a sort of high-level introduction to the process, defining all the pieces of the process at a high level. Let's take a moment and examine the various components of the process as defined by ISO 9001:2015:

- *Inputs and outputs.* This is exactly what it sounds like. Inputs are usually received from other preceding processes, and could include physical or informational resources. The outputs are the products that result from the process or the services that are performed. These could be intermediate products or services, as opposed to something a customer would actually pay for. If you think of a process model as flowing from left to right, then you can imagine the inputs on the left side and output on the right side.

- *Sequence and interaction.* Even the simplest organizations have multiple processes. ISO 9001:2015 asks you to sequentially order these processes. So the design process would come before the purchasing process, the purchasing process would come before the production process, and so on.

- *Criteria and methods.* The criteria for the process is how it will be judged. This is basically the requirements that the process is attempting to meet. Methods are the procedures that must be used in the operation of the process. The measurements and performance indicators are what will tell you if the process is meeting the criteria you established or not.

- *Resources.* These could include raw materials, supplies, specifications, utilities, or any number of things. Many processes begin, only to stop abruptly when it's determined that a key resource is missing. The intent of this is to prevent this from happening. Resources are planned and acquired in advance, and they meet all the requirements of the process.

- *Responsibility and authority.* Simply put, someone is responsible for each process. This is the primary responsibility and authority for the process, but there may be other responsibilities stated on the tasks level. For example, there might be a responsibility and authority for procuring materials, a responsibility and authority for inspecting the final product, and responsibility and authority for communicating with the customer. At a minimum, you must state who is in charge of the overall process.

- *Risks and opportunities.* This subclause specifically addresses the requirements of clause 6.1, which is where we are asked to determine risks and opportunities within ISO 9001:2015. You really have to address clause 6.1 first and then come back to clause 4.4 to complete your process description. In describing your process, it would make sense if you only list the major risks and opportunities that influence the process. Listing everything would make for a very cluttered process model.

- *Evaluation.* How will you know that the process is effective? Your process model should state your intended result and how you're able to monitor and/or measure the result. The evaluation is nothing more than comparing actual results to intended results and identifying that gap.

- *Improvement.* Here, you might define potential categories of improvement for the process in question. These could include cost reductions, efficiency improvements, fewer nonconformities, higher customer satisfaction, or any number of other measures. When determining opportunities for improvement, think about the specific process in question, and especially consider the risks and opportunities that were determined in clause 6.1. These should guide you to the most meaningful improvements.

The output of this little exercise is a comprehensive understanding of what is needed to operate your processes. To be fully sustainable, this understanding should be maintained as documented information. Process documentation isn't specifically required by ISO 9001:2015, however. The words "to the extent necessary" are mentioned twice in this section of the standard. This gives you a great deal of discretion in how you document your process and in what records you might keep. Very simple processes may not require a process description like the one we've described in this chapter. Likewise, records may not be necessary if the process outputs are insignificant.

As you define your processes, keep in mind that this isn't intended to be an academic exercise. The point is to gain a practical understanding of the management, control, and improvement of your processes. A process approach should always be considered when writing or revising documentation. Even though ISO 9001:2015 does not mandate that all processes be documented in this manner, your organization's risks and opportunities will guide you in knowing which processes should be documented.

We can talk about processes all day long, but it might be more helpful to actually see one.

Figure 2.3 provides an example of a process depicted as a turtle diagram. Figure 2.4 shows a process matrix, which is a great way to capture all of an organization's processes in one convenient location.

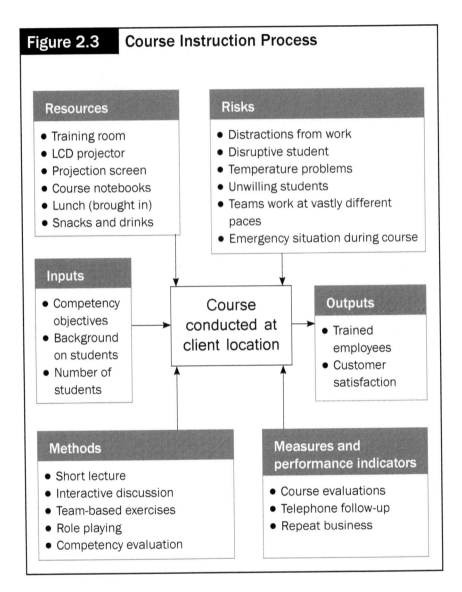

Figure 2.3   Course Instruction Process

Resources
- Training room
- LCD projector
- Projection screen
- Course notebooks
- Lunch (brought in)
- Snacks and drinks

Risks
- Distractions from work
- Disruptive student
- Temperature problems
- Unwilling students
- Teams work at vastly different paces
- Emergency situation during course

Inputs
- Competency objectives
- Background on students
- Number of students

Course conducted at client location

Outputs
- Trained employees
- Customer satisfaction

Methods
- Short lecture
- Interactive discussion
- Team-based exercises
- Role playing
- Competency evaluation

Measures and performance indicators
- Course evaluations
- Telephone follow-up
- Repeat business

Figure 2.4	Sample Process Matrix: Champion Metal Forming Inc.					
Process	**Inputs**	**Criteria and methods**	**Resources**	**Outputs**	**Risks** (see also risks and opportunity analysis)	**Measures and performance indicators**
1. Planning **Responsibility: CEO**	• Research • Results of brainstorming • Customer list • Regulatory list • Historical performance	• Identify internal issues • Identify external issues • Interview interested parties • Identify risks and opportunities • Plan of changes • Strategic planning • Develop quality objectives • Determine planning for objectives	• Conference room • Flipcharts • Top management leadership • Time	• Quality objectives • Understanding context of organization • Strategic plan • Understanding interested parties • QMS scope	• In a rush to finish • Inadequate research	• Internal audit results • Revenue growth • Net income growth
2. Sales **Responsibility: VP of sales**	• Sales literature • Pricing schedules • Customer needs	• Provide specifications • Prepare quotes • Answer customer inquiries • Take orders • Review orders • Send to scheduling	• ERP software • CRM software • Travel budget • Marketing support • Teleconferencing • Company website	• Customer orders • Clearly defined requirements	• Missing sales forecast • Competitors • Late orders • Customer complaints	• Revenue growth • Net income growth
3. Scheduling **Responsibility: VP of operations**	• Customer orders • Manufacturing capacity • Feedback from all functions	• Prioritize orders • Maintain stock levels • Combine jobs in order to maximize efficiency • Publish manufacturing schedule • Amend schedule	• ERP software • Master plant layout • Process standards	• Manufacturing schedule	• Downtime • Unbalanced schedule • Rush orders	• Percentage of on-time delivery to customer • Manufacturing efficiency

Figure 2.4	Sample Process Matrix: Champion Metal Forming Inc. (Cont.)					
Process	Inputs	Criteria and methods	Resources	Outputs	Risks (see also risks and opportunity analysis)	Measures and performance indicators
4. Purchasing **Responsibility:** **Director of** **supply chain**	• Requirements from all functions • Pricing information • Historical supplier performance	• Qualify suppliers • Monitor supplier performance • Process purchase orders • Maintain approved supplier list • Improve supplier performance	• ERP software • Conference room • Internet for supplier research • Approved supplier list	• Purchased product • Data on supplier performance	• Cost increases • Supplier disruptions • Inadequate supplier capabilities • In-transit damage	• Percentage of on-time delivery • Net income growth
5. Receiving **Responsibility:** **Director of** **supply chain**	• Product requirements on purchase orders • Purchased products	• Verify incoming product • Stage materials in warehouse • Communicate status to purchasing • Process nonconforming products as needed	• Receiving area • Nonconforming cage • Dimensional measuring instruments	• Conforming products • Records of incoming inspection	• Late deliveries • Nonconforming product • Missing nonconformities during inspection	• Manufacturing efficiency • No lost-time accidents • Net income growth
6. Manufacturing **Responsibility:** **VP of** **operations**	• Production schedule • Product specifications • Purchased supplies and materials	• Stamping • Finishing • Assembly • Inspect and test	• Stamping press • Dies • Grinders • Forklift • QC Lab	• Final product • Test data	• Equipment downtime • Nonconforming product • Injuries • Scrap material • Waste • Missing nonconformities during inspection	• Percentage of on-time delivery • Manufacturing efficiency • No lost-time accidents • Net income growth

Figure 2.4	Sample Process Matrix: Champion Metal Forming Inc. (Cont.)					
Process	**Inputs**	**Criteria and methods**	**Resources**	**Outputs**	**Risks** (see also risks and opportunity analysis)	**Measures and performance indicators**
7. Shipping **Responsibility:** Director of supply chain	• Production schedule • Final product • Shipping supplies	• Package products • Label • Prepare test data with shipping • Schedule trucks • Ship to customers • Monitor shipments	• Shipping docks • Packaging • Cardboard cartons • Wooden pallets • Label printer	• Shipped product • No damage	• Late shipments • Inadequate packaging • Mishandling • Wrong item shipped • Paperwork wrong	• Percentage of on-time delivery • No lost-time accidents • Net income growth
8. Document and record control **Responsibility:** Director of supply chain	• Document control procedure • Record control procedure	• Control documents • Ensure accessibility • Ensure periodic review of documents • Maintain records	• Computer server • Computer network	• Valid documents • Accessible records	• Obsolete documents available • Revisions not published • Records deleted • Records misfiled	• Internal audit results
9. Training and development **Responsibility:** Director of supply chain	• Competency requirements • Gaps in personal competency • Training checklists	• Assist in determining competency requirements • Provide training • Evaluate effectiveness • Develop new training • Administer OJT program • Administer new employee orientation • Maintain records	• Training room • Projector • LMS software • Budget for food and snacks • Top management leadership	• Increased skills, knowledge, and understanding • More effectiveness • Records of training	• Competency not achieved • Too busy to train • New skills not included in training	• Internal audit results

Figure 2.4	Sample Process Matrix: Champion Metal Forming Inc. (Cont.)					
Process	**Inputs**	**Criteria and methods**	**Resources**	**Outputs**	**Risks** (see also risks and opportunity analysis)	**Measures and performance indicators**
10. Management review Responsibility: CEO	• Data • Information • Ideas • Problems • Opportunities	• Analyze data • Discuss issues • Determine actions and decisions	• Conference room • Color laser printer • Projector • Top management leadership	• Actions • Decisions • Improvements • Management review records	• Top management not engaged • Too busy • No follow-through on action items • Inaccurate data	• Revenue growth • Net income growth • Internal audit results
11. Improvement processes Responsibility: VP of operations	• Customer feedback • Data • Trends • Nonconformities • Opportunities	• Corrective action • Objectives • Customer satisfaction • Internal auditing	• Time • Training and development • Top management leadership	• Improvement • Customer loyalty • Long-term success	• Too busy • Failure to follow through • No training on improvement tools	• Revenue growth • Net income growth • Internal audit results

4.4 FREQUENTLY ASKED QUESTIONS

Does all our documentation have to be in a process format, such as a fishbone (cause-and-effect) diagram?

No, you can choose whatever format works best for you. At a high level, you do have to define all the variables shown in subclause 4.4.1(a–g). An easy and visual way to do this is through a fishbone diagram.

Does subclause 4.4.2(a) require that we maintain documented information on every process?

No. You have to determine where documentation is necessary.

Chapter 3

ISO 9001:2015 Section 5 Leadership

5.1 LEADERSHIP AND COMMITMENT

5.1.1 General

Similar to clause 5.1 in ISO 9001:2008, but many new requirements were added.

This section provides an introduction to the topic of leadership within the context of the quality management system (QMS) and beyond. The 2008 version of ISO 9001 included just four items that top management was required to demonstrate commitment to, but the 2015 version asks leadership to commit to 11 different items. What does that tell you about the topic of leadership? It gains in importance every time ISO 9001 is revised. The current list of commitments in ISO 9001:2015 is impressive in that it really puts leadership front and center in the QMS.

Let's take a look at each commitment and discuss how top management might address each one.

- *Be accountable for the QMS.* This is a new and powerful requirement. It tells leadership that they are ultimately responsibility for the outcome of the QMS. If things don't work out as expected, it's not the responsibility of the quality manager, lab supervisor, shift leader, or anybody else. All roads lead back to leadership. The intent is that top management take an active role in the functioning of the QMS. Management review will be one of the key tools for making this happen.

A number of the next requirements for top management start with the word "ensuring." This means that top managers ensure that these things happen. They may not perform the task themselves, but at the very least they delegate the tasks and review the outcome of the work. Top management should be able to talk intimately about all these topics and explain how their leadership and commitment drove the processes forward.

- *Make sure a quality policy and objectives are in place and are consistent with the organization's strategy.* This sentence contains multiple requirements. First, top management ensures that there is a quality policy and quality objectives. Because these two documents are so foundational, it's very likely that top management would take a hands-on role in developing them. Second, the policy and objectives must agree with the strategic direction of the organization. That requires, of course, that there be a strategic direction, which is usually defined in a business plan, strategic plan, budget, or some other executive planning tool. If the strategic plan includes big actions, then it would be appropriate for the quality policy and objectives to mirror those actions in some way, possibly by mentioning them or providing metrics that lead in the same direction.

  The policy and objectives also need to be congruent with the context of the organization that was determined in clause 4.1. If the environmental scanning required in clause 4.1 revealed that hazardous waste disposal was the most important issue facing the company, then the policy and objectives should reflect this. All we're doing here is making sure that all of our high-level documents agree with each other. Top management should be comfortable explaining and illustrating this.

- *Make sure that the QMS is used to help manage the business.* This is a new requirement in ISO 9001:2015. Unfortunately, QMSs often exist in a vacuum, disconnected from the rest of the organization's decision making. The QMS processes are the way that we should holistically manage our organizations, and they must be fully incorporated into our business processes. For instance, the corrective action required by ISO 9001 is how we solve problems within the organization. Management review is how top management reviews data and information and makes decisions. Internal auditing is how we ensure process discipline. Get the idea? In short, we're not implementing ISO 9001:2015 just to get certified, we're implementing the standard to manage our business. Top management should be able to demonstrate how ISO 9001:2015 processes are the true business processes within the organization, not puppet processes to impress an auditor.

- *Advocate the process approach and how risk affects the business.* This is a completely new requirement in ISO 9001:2015. First, it requires that top management be advocates for the process approach. Recall clause 4.4, which requires that processes be formally determined and defined. The process approach means that we manage activities from start to finish, considering all the process activities that they represent, including inputs/outputs, resources, monitoring, measurement, improvement, training, and other considerations. We don't just try to manage one or two pieces of the process, we understand and manage all parts of the process. Risk-based thinking is the second part of the requirement. Risks and opportunities are addressed in clause 6.1 of the standard. The philosophy behind risk-based thinking is that we apply our resources in a proactive manner and as efficiently as possible. It follows these steps:
  1. Scan the environment and objectively look inward at the organization.
  2. Identify the organization's risks and opportunities.
  3. Determine which risks and opportunities are the most significant.
  4. Determine actions to proactively manage the risks and opportunities.
  5. Continually evaluate the effectiveness of the actions to address risks and opportunities.

- *Make sure that resources are available for the functioning of the QMS.* Nothing happens without resources, and it's usually top management who provides them. Through existing processes like strategic planning and management review, the need for resources is identified and a plan is developed for their provision. Top management should address how resources have been determined and provided, giving specific examples as they relate to the QMS.

- *Tell everybody how important the QMS is and why it's critical to conform to its requirements.* This is a communication requirement that is directly fulfilled by top management. Leadership doesn't delegate this one. They are effectively saying, "Hey, this ISO 9001 stuff is real and I believe in it. You should believe in it, too." This message could be delivered in a variety of ways, with in-person probably being the most effective. Besides just talking the talk, actually demonstrating involvement in the QMS goes even further. Top management's involvement in the following processes will communicate more than words ever could:
  - ✓ Motivating and participating in corrective action
  - ✓ Analyzing customer feedback
  - ✓ Assisting in the identification of risks and opportunities
  - ✓ Participating in internal audits, either as an auditor or an auditee
  - ✓ Evaluating progress against quality objectives and helping to develop plans for their achievement
  - ✓ Adding to organizational knowledge
  - ✓ Leading management review and sharing the results with the rest of the organization

- *Make sure that the QMS produces the expected outcomes.* A QMS consumes considerable resources to implement and maintain, so there should be some payback. This payback is in the form of planned results, such as less waste, higher customer satisfaction, and higher profits. The most obvious way for top management to monitor intended results would be through tracking the progress of quality objectives. Participating in management review and reviewing QMS data streams would be two other ways.

- *Show leadership in getting employees involved in the QMS.* This is another requirement that asks top management to get engaged in an area in which it might not have previously been involved. Top management must have direct oversight with the people involved with the ISO 9001 effort. The most obvious way to satisfy this requirement would be through vigorous participation during management review and in carefully analyzing all its inputs.

- *Encourage improvement activities.* This is a completely new requirement. It actually includes a couple of different requirements. Top managers must be aware of the improvement efforts within the organization. Then they must communicate their support and promotion of the improvement efforts. A more hands-on way of meeting the requirement would be for top management to directly participate in improvement activities, though this isn't always possible. Participation on at least a periodic basis is well worth the time and effort.

- *Assist other managers in showing QMS leadership.* This requirement asks top management to get other managers "whipped into shape." Middle management is frequently one of the weakest parts of the organization. Middle managers have the power to throw up many obstacles to efforts and processes that they don't believe in. They are much more likely to support the QMS, though, if top management emphasizes that their support is needed and they must participate in a positive way.

Many of the requirements for top management's leadership are redundant. Achieving one of them is likely to actually achieve two or three. Beyond just meeting requirements, top management's direct involvement is absolutely necessary to have a successful QMS.

5.1.1 FREQUENTLY ASKED QUESTIONS

There are numerous aspects of leadership and commitment that top management must demonstrate in subclause 5.1.1. Do we have to keep records of top management's compliance?

ISO 9001:2015 doesn't require you to retain documented information (i.e., keep records) of this. If there's a different way of showing that they met the commitments, then that would suffice as evidence. In the absence of records, ask a variety of personnel how the commitments were met and how top management demonstrated leadership. And, of course, ask top management how they demonstrated leadership and commitment over the QMS. Their own words will reveal a lot.

5.1.1 FREQUENTLY ASKED QUESTIONS

Top management of our organization is the vice president of operations, but she has designated that the plant manager act as top management for ISO 9001:2015 purposes. Is this OK?

No. Top management is whoever leads your organization at the highest levels within the defined QMS scope. This can't be delegated downward.

5.1.2 Customer focus

Equivalent to clause 5.2 of ISO 9001:2008, with the addition of risks and opportunities.

Customer focus is the awareness of who the customers are, their strategic importance, and their needs and expectations. Customers are the reason for the organization's existence, and it's top management's job to drive this point home. When everybody in the organization shares a customer focus, they have unity of purpose and all work in the same direction.

Customer focus was required in ISO 9001:2008, but it was just a single sentence of not much consequence. In ISO 9001:2015, the requirement has been expanded considerably. Top management must now show leadership in four points of customer focus. All the requirements of this section ask top management to "ensure" that certain things happen. They might not actually perform these tasks, but rather perform an oversight or communications role. All the requirements of this section can be met by effectively addressing other parts of the standard. In other words, the requirements don't stand on their own as discrete requirements. Let's discuss each of the requirements for customer focus.

Top management will make sure that customer requirements and applicable statutory and regulatory requirements are determined and met.

In small organizations, top management is personally involved in determining and meeting customer requirements. However, in most organizations top management empowers others to determine and meet customer requirements. As long as top management has ensured that this happens, the spirit of the requirement has been met. Top management achieves this primarily through ensuring resources are provided for the following activities:

- Staffing positions that determine customer requirements
- Clearly defining responsibilities and authorities for customer service and sales
- Training personnel in customer communications
- Developing procedures for taking orders and product realization
- Ensuring the customer requirements are reviewed for accuracy and completeness

The second part of this requirement concerns statutory and regulatory requirements. These types of specialized requirements are most often determined by a technical or legal function, as they are beyond the grasp of most laymen. Examples might include laws, regulations, and statutes that govern the following:

- Product safety
- Product performance requirements
- Product labeling
- Fuel standards
- The use of certain ingredients or raw materials
- Warranty requirements
- Product flammability

It's quite rare for top management to personally determine these requirements, but they would certainly empower others to do so. As long as top management makes sure that these requirements are met and that roles have been assigned for the tasks, then the requirement is met.

Top management will make sure that risks and opportunities affecting products, services, and customer satisfaction are determined and acted upon.

This is a new requirement in ISO 9001:2015. It stems from the risk-based nature of ISO 9001:2015, specifically the risks and opportunities related to products and customer satisfaction. The very survival of the organization requires that we address these in a meaningful and effective way. Top management can ensure this by reviewing the action plans that address risks and making sure that adequate resources are available for their implementation. Actions to address risks and opportunities are a required input to management review, so if top management is participating (and leading) management review, this should happen automatically.

Top management will ensure that the focus on consistently providing products and services that meet customer and applicable statutory and regulatory requirements is maintained. This can be accomplished by ensuring that effective inspection and verification processors are in place. Support of the internal audit process will also reinforce this focus.

Top management will make sure that the organization focuses on creating customer satisfaction.

A focus on customer satisfaction is usually accomplished through communicating about customer perceptions. This means opening up direct communication lines with the customer and asking hard questions. What have we done well lately? What have we not done well? What could make you want to seek a different supplier? These questions and answers should be regular discussion points led by top management.

Nearly all the requirements of this section can be met through simple oversight and communication. These requirements also connect to stronger requirements in other parts of the standard. As long as top management is involved in a two-way conversation on these topics—receiving and analyzing information, and then sharing information with other parts of the organization—they will have met the requirement.

5.1.2 FREQUENTLY ASKED QUESTIONS

Do I need to do anything specific in this section? It seems like we would satisfy 5.1.2 by implementing other parts of the ISO 9001:2015 standard.

You don't need to do anything specific unless you see the need to do so. This section of ISO 9001 is often met through achievement of other requirements.

We would like to introduce the concept of internal customers to our employees. Can we do this as part of ISO 9001:2015?

Yes, of course. The concept of internal customers is very powerful, though it's not specifically addressed by ISO 9001:2015.

5.2 POLICY

Equivalent to clause 5.3 in ISO 9001:2008, with some minor additions.

The quality policy is top management's overall direction and philosophy related to quality. It's typically a short document, often fewer than 100 words. The policy is often structured as a series of bulleted commitments, though you could adapt whatever format is appropriate. The quality policy communicates to everyone in the organization what's truly important to the organization's success. You aren't obligated to call your quality policy by that name. It could just as well be called a mission statement, vision, charter, statement of excellence, or any number of other names. In fact, there are good reasons for not using the word "quality" as part of its name, since quality has a very narrowly defined meaning in some organizations.

Some organizations expand the use of the quality policy by covering such items as culture, values, ethics, and other attributes. There's certainly nothing wrong with this. As long as you address the minimum requirements, you can add whatever else you feel is appropriate. Just make sure that you're able to demonstrate each of the commitments that you include in your quality policy. Even though it's a very high-level document, the quality policy is still a document and, as such, it constitutes a set of auditable requirements. Don't include idle "pie in the sky" declarations that sound good but have no practical relevance to your organization.

Here are some questions you can ask top management to establish the quality policy:

- As an organization, what do we really believe in?
- What are we striving for?
- What role does the customer play in our success formula?
- What does the word "quality" really mean to us?
- What makes our products better than similar products?
- What words would you use to summarize our organizational culture?

These questions are likely to elicit a wide range of very inspirational and stirring themes. Take these themes, temper them with a healthy dose of realism, and you probably have some themes that can be included in your quality policy.

5.2 FREQUENTLY ASKED QUESTIONS

How does our quality policy support our strategic direction?

The policy is the uppermost document in your QMS, and it influences other high-level documents. For example, if you have a strategy to design certain products, the quality policy might state that innovation is a key principle. If you have a strategy for building a new facility, the policy might state that growth and/or expansion was important. The quality policy provides a stepping stone to strategic direction and quality objectives.

5.2 FREQUENTLY ASKED QUESTIONS

Do we need to actually say in our quality policy that it will be communicated, understood, applied, and available to interested parties?

Not unless you want to. Those are requirements related to implementing the policy, not commitments that must be stated within the policy.

Does the quality policy have to be signed by top management?

No. There must be some evidence of top management's approval, but this could be demonstrated through meeting minutes, approval of the quality manual, or other means.

5.2.1 Establishing the quality policy

ISO 9001:2015 makes it clear that the quality policy originates from top management. It's common to have middle managers or quality professionals facilitate the development of the quality policy, but ultimately the policy should represent top management's true direction and intent on quality. Top management should be able to talk about the policy and give examples of how its actions model commitments. The standard also says that the policy must be reviewed. This is typically done at least once a year during management review or some other high-level leadership forum. Finally, the first sentence says that the quality policy must be maintained, and this is accomplished by communicating it to employees and using it as a guide for action.

Your policy must meet the following requirements:

- *Fits the organization's purpose, environment, and strategy.* This means that the quality policy relates to the core purpose and activities of the organization. In fact, it may briefly describe what the organization does. Keep in mind that most quality policies are fewer than 100 words, so this description will be very brief. If there are special concerns (such as safety for an organization that manufactures dynamite, or confidentiality for an organization that performs mental health services), then these concerns must also be addressed in the policy. That is the "context" that the standard mentions. A generic quality policy wouldn't satisfy these special requirements. If your quality policy could be adopted by ACME Widget Co. without any changes, then you need to rewrite it. The final few words of this section really emphasize the need for a highly customized and specific quality policy. Every organization's strategic direction will be different, and its quality policy should support it.

- *Gives direction for determining quality objectives.* The quality policy, either directly or indirectly, must provide guidance for setting objectives. This can be satisfied by including language such as, "We are committed to establishing and reviewing objectives as part of our continual improvement effort," or it could be satisfied by the implication of measurable objectives. However, don't include your specific objectives within your quality policy. Objectives are subject to change on a regular basis, and the policy is more of a thematic document that will change less frequently.

- *Commits to meeting applicable requirements.* The term "applicable requirements" is quite vague. This is interpreted to mean requirements that exist within the scope of ISO 9001:2015. It's not necessary to individually list these requirements, as that would make an exceptionally long quality policy. You simply make a commitment to satisfy applicable requirements. The proof of meeting the requirements is embodied within the remainder of the QMS.

- *Commits to continually improving the QMS.* This means exactly what it says. The organization must commit to continual improvement. The easiest and most obvious way to do this is to use these exact words in your policy, although you could certainly paraphrase the commitment or put your own spin on it. As with the previous commitment, the true evidence of improvement will be woven throughout the system.

5.2.2 Communicating the quality policy

A quality policy is worthless without maintenance and communication. The current version must always be available and employees must comprehend it. Just because the policy is short doesn't mean anybody will truly understand it or know how it should be applied on a day-to-day basis. Treat your quality policy like the uppermost document in your QMS, not just some random one-page missive. Make sure to address the following points with the implementation of your policy:

- *The quality policy must be accessible and documented.* This means that it's a formal document and subject to document control. It will have a revision level and be approved by top management. Some organizations even go as far as putting document numbers on their quality policies, though a title is usually adequate. "Accessible" means that it's available to employees and that they can demonstrate how they access it.

- *The quality policy must be shared openly, comprehended by employees, and utilized within the organization.* ISO 9001 has always required that the quality policy be available to and understood by employees. ISO 9001:2015 adds an additional requirement that the policy be applied or utilized. Let's examine the entire requirement. First, the policy is communicated. That means exactly what it says. Tell people about the policy, explain what it means, and describe how it applies to people's jobs. This isn't rocket science. Most quality policies fit on a single screen or sheet of paper, so this could be covered during a company meeting or some other forum. "Understood" means that the employees received and absorbed the message. If an auditor were to ask an employee what the quality policy means to him or her, the employee should be able to say a few words about it and how he or she supports it in day-to-day activities. Keep in mind that employees don't need to memorize the quality policy to understand it. "Applied" simply means that we use the quality policy as a central beacon of purpose within the organization. We apply the quality policy by reminding ourselves that it exists and making sure that our actions support its intent and commitments. Top management doesn't have to be the entity communicating the quality policy to the rest of the organization, but many people would argue that it's more effective if it does.

- *Be accessible to interested parties.* This is the new requirement related to the quality policy. It's up to the organization to decide when and how it's appropriate to share the quality policy with interested parties. You could decide, for instance, to make your quality policy available if somebody enters your lobby or visits your website. This would be a very simple and unobtrusive way to meet the requirement. The whole point is to allow interested parties to understand what your organization is committing itself to.

Nothing lasts forever, not even a quality policy. The passage of time can render any policy obsolete. A typical approach is that top management review the quality policy at least once a year, although organizations could certainly review it more often. The management review function is the most common forum for reviewing the quality policy.

Ecolink Inc.'s Quality Policy and Cultural Norms

Ecolink Inc. is small company, but you won't find a Fortune 100 company that takes its organizational culture more seriously. Located in Tucker, Georgia, Ecolink (*www.ecolink.com*) develops and formulates industrial degreasers and solvents. Maybe not a glamorous business, but Ecolink long ago saw an opportunity to leverage its environmental stewardship and help customers make smart choices.

"Sustainability is simply the right thing to do," explains Ecolink President John Roudebush. "Secondly, it gives us a huge opportunity to tap into new business. We get a lot of new customers by saying, 'We're here to sell you less and safer chemicals.' It's a message that really resonates with the environmental, health, and safety community."

Focusing on the reduction of environmental impacts became one of the driving themes of Ecolink's business. When the company implemented ISO 9001, it wanted a quality policy that really set the tone for its business practices and strategy. Environmentalism was one of the key principles that was stressed. Never mind that it was a "quality" policy, the point was that this was a major part of Ecolink's business strategy and it needed to be highlighted in the company's policy. As Roudebush led the company through the development of the quality policy, other important themes emerged. These included work-life balance, positive karma, and high integrity and ethics. The final result was a wide-ranging and unique quality policy that truly fit the organization it was written for.

| **Figure 3.1** | Sample Quality Policy |

Ecolink Inc.
Quality Policy and Core Values

Ecolink Inc. is committed to providing environmentally preferred industrial degreasers and solvents. In pursuit of this, we are dedicated to the following points:

- Create an environment of integrity and high ethics
- Help customers use safer chemicals and less chemicals through a philosophy of common sense environmentalism
- Establish objectives to help communicate organizational direction and drive improvements
- Meet or exceed our customers' expectations and all other relevant requirements
- Instill a culture of positive karma, whereby we unselfishly try to help others
- Communicate leaner chemical solutions for the next generation
- Achieve continual improvement of our operations and performance
- Live our lives in a balanced way, working hard for the company, but never sacrificing quality of life at home.

Used by permission. Copyright 2015 Ecolink Inc. *www.ecolink.com.*

Roudebush decided that he wanted to go one step further than the quality policy. What sort of employee behaviors would reinforce the principles the company was founded on? This led to the development of the Ecolink Behavioral/Cultural Norms. They represent a natural extension of the quality policy, but define actions and behaviors that could be put into practice every minute of the day. Over the years the Behavioral/Cultural Norms grew to 25 specific actions that reinforce the organizational culture that Roudebush has established. These include such principles as "Check your ego at the door," "Do what's best for the client," and "Create a feeling of warmth in every interaction."

To make sure that every employee understands the Behavioral/Cultural Norms, Ecolink maintains a weekly schedule that allows each employee an opportunity to discuss what a norm means to him or her. The employees bring the concepts to life through practical examples of how the norms guide their actions.

So, when an auditor asks, "How do you communicate and support your quality policy?" Roudebush tells them to sit back and relax. It might take a while.

5.3 ORGANIZATIONAL ROLES, RESPONSIBILITIES AND AUTHORITIES

Equivalent to subclauses 5.5.1 and 5.5.2 in ISO 9001:2008. The term "management representative" is gone, but the responsibilities are still listed.

Defined responsibilities and authorities are one of the hallmarks of a QMS. Responsibility is what personnel must do, and authority is what they are empowered to do. When roles, responsibilities, and authorities are clear there is less confusion and more efficiency. How many times have you heard the following statements?

- *That's not my responsibility.*
- *Nobody's really in charge of this.*
- *We have some confusion around who does what.*
- *I have a lot of responsibility but no authority.*
- *The ball gets dropped a lot around here.*
- *We have too many chiefs and no Indians.*

These are all symptoms that responsibilities and authorities may not be clearly defined and communicated. It's worth noting that this section of ISO 9001:2015 doesn't explicitly say that responsibilities and authorities must be documented. Only the smallest organizations could effectively communicate responsibilities and authorities without some sort of documentation. Job descriptions are a common way of meeting this requirement, though they are certainly not required. If your human resources department already has job descriptions on file, it could be a simple matter of making sure that they're current. You'll also need to apply a document control procedure to them, since they are within the scope of the management system. Procedures can also effectively communicate responsibilities and authorities.

A lot of responsibilities in this clause of ISO 9001:2015 were formally responsibilities of the entity known as the management representative. That role is no longer mentioned in the standard, but obviously it still has relevance and its responsibilities remain. An organization may opt to continue to have a management representative, but this isn't required. However, each of the responsibilities and authorities required in clause 5.3 must be assigned to somebody.

Let's take a look at each of these responsibilities and authorities, and discuss how they might be performed.

Responsibility for making sure that the QMS meets ISO 9001:2015's requirements

Somebody has to make sure that the organization is adhering to the standard's requirements. Everybody in the organization contributes to this outcome, but some responsible individual must have an oversight role. Personnel assigned this responsibility often go by the titles quality engineer, quality manager, or director of quality, though this certainly doesn't have to be a "quality" person. Anybody with an understanding of ISO 9001:2015 and its application could fill the role. Some of the specific ways this is done include:

- Using ISO 9001:2015 as a model for establishing the system.
- Conducting internal audits to ensure that processes meet the standard.
- Receiving training on the practical application of ISO 9001:2015 and passing this knowledge along to others within the organization.
- Keeping the organization as a whole informed on the QMS and how it relates to ISO 9001:2015.

Responsibility for making sure that processes produce effective outputs

In other words, are we getting the right results? The first step toward this is defining the processes in the first place. Once we have defined processes, we can establish performance indicators or objectives that will tell us if the process is delivering the intended results. The performance of each process is compared against the objective that's been set for it, and we know whether we're on track. This role is really one of measurement and reporting. It can be done by one person or multiple people, but the evidence of it happening is usually some kind of data that top management can examine and draw conclusions from. Sound like an important responsibility? It is.

Responsibility for reporting on the QMS and improvement opportunities to top management

This is another role that can be summarized by one word: reporting. The person performing this role is a conduit through which data flows. It's not raw data, but rather data that have been converted into information by arranging them in a meaningful way or through a graphic depiction. The person assigned this responsibility should be good at summarizing information, facilitating its analysis, and driving toward specific improvement actions. It's not a passive role, but a very active coaching role that specifically involves top management. In fact, the last few words of this requirement allude to the fact that somebody must be responsible for leading the management review.

Responsibility for driving a customer focus throughout the company

Customer focus should be a natural thing. After all, that's the reason for the organization's existence. However, the larger and more complex organizations become, the more hidden the customer becomes. Gradually, people begin to forget that customers even exist. The purpose of this role is to not let that happen. The person assigned this responsibility can perform a number of specific tasks to create this awareness:
- Ensure that customer feedback is being collected and analyzed.
- Communicate the results of customer feedback.
- Ensure that the organization records, acts on, and learns from customer complaints.
- Facilitate process improvements that aid customers.

- Drive an awareness of internal customer relationships.
- Encourage and facilitate product innovation.

Responsibility for ensuring that the QMS stays effective when changes occur

This means that the QMS can't be allowed to slip. Many of the previous roles were reporting responsibilities, but this role is definitely an enforcing responsibility. People in organizations love to make tweaks and changes to processes, but the last thing that's on their mind is the integrity of the QMS. This role ensures that we consider the QMS any time we make changes by asking some of these questions:

- Should we write a new document?
- Should we revise an existing document?
- Should training take place?
- Should top management communicate something?
- Should we begin measuring something, or perhaps even stop measuring something?

This role asks these questions, and many others, and then makes sure that we have reasonable answers for each of them.

5.3 FREQUENTLY ASKED QUESTIONS

Can we use an organizational chart to define responsibility and authority?

Probably not. An organizational chart usually shows reporting relationships and organizational structure, not responsibilities and authorities.

ISO 9001:2015 no longer requires an ISO 9001 management representative. Is it OK if we continue to have one?

Yes, of course. The term "management representative" is gone from ISO 9001:2015, but the responsibilities and authorities are still included.

Chapter 4

ISO 9001:2015 Section 6 Planning

6.1 ACTIONS TO ADDRESS RISKS AND OPPORTUNITIES

6.1.1 (No subclause title)

No equivalent requirements in ISO 9001:2008, though inspired by subclauses 8.5.3 and 5.4.2.

Risk management could be the single most significant addition to ISO 9001:2015. It requires a complete change of focus in implementing a quality management system (QMS). Instead of just mindlessly implementing the "shalls" of the standard, the organization has to identify and control its unique risks and opportunities. Most organizations do this anyway, at least unconsciously. ISO 9001:2015 requires a fully conscious and planned approach to risk management. If implemented correctly, it will become one of the most powerful processes in the organization.

Risk management sounds intimidating. Many people reading these words are probably thinking, "This is going to be such a pain to implement." Actually, risk management can be put into place with just a modest effort. The alternative to risk management is far worse. What is it? Crisis management, of course. If you don't bother to manage risks, you'd better be very good at handling crises. The investment you make in risk management is going to be much less than the cost and time necessary to handle full-blown problems.

Risk management has a variety of benefits:

- *It increases everybody's awareness of risk.* Employees at all levels begin thinking about risk in their day-to-day activities. In the process, they become better stewards of the company's resources and fully engaged partners in its success.

- *It focuses our effort on the things that matter most.* A good risk management system reveals significant risks and opportunities. We can then apply a proportionate amount of control to the risks that are most threatening.

- *It helps create a culture of prevention and risk management.* An organization's culture changes slowly and gradually. A risk management process will gradually affect the way everybody thinks. It won't discourage risk-taking, but it will encourage "informed" risk taking. All decisions are made with an understanding of the inherent risk and potential benefits.

- *It helps make us more successful.* The ultimate result of a risk management system is more success and less failure. The crises that seem to pop up frequently at poorly managed organizations don't happen as much in an organization that has a risk management process.

Before we go much further, we should define risk. Risk is anything that can affect our ability to achieve the organization's objectives. Risks can be good or bad, but uncertainty is always involved. We can never know for sure if a risk is going to occur or how it will affect us.

Where do the risks and opportunities come from? They originate from brainstorming. You already have some very good raw material for this examination of risks. Our raw material are clauses 4.1 and 4.2 of ISO 9001:2015. You certainly remember clause 4.1, in which we identified internal and external issues relevant to our strategy. This was framed in the context of strengths, weaknesses, opportunities, and threats. The weaknesses and threats we identified obviously equate to risks. The remainder of the internal and external issues comprise the opportunities category.

The other raw material for our analysis of risk and opportunities is interested parties. Specifically, what do these interested parties require of us? This was identified in clause 4.2 of ISO 9001:2015. Each requirement may constitute a risk, an opportunity, or a combination of both. There is a third input to your risks and opportunities: corrective actions. Corrective actions are aimed at removing causes of nonconformity and ultimately removing risk. If you do a good job of corrective actions, your overall risk will be reduced.

So, in reality, you've already done a lot of work on risks and opportunities. It might be helpful now to divide the output of clauses 4.1 and 4.2 into two big categories: risks and opportunities. Our challenge now is to evaluate the significance of the risks and opportunities. They are not all created equal. Some risks can kill people or put us out of business, while others may be nothing more than a nuisance. Likewise, some opportunities will ensure long-term success, while others just provide a temporary positive bump.

We need a way of evaluating the risk and opportunities, because we don't have enough time or money to act on all of them. ISO 9001:2015 gives us that leeway. It explicitly says that the organization shall "determine risks and opportunities that need to be addressed." Clearly, not all risks and opportunities need to be addressed, just the ones that you determine to be the most significant. Without rating them in some manner, you won't have any way of knowing which risks and opportunities deserve the most attention. Figure 4.1 shows a sample rating scheme for evaluating your risks. Obviously, you might need to customize it for your own unique circumstances. Please note that it's common to rate risks in a quantitative manner, but opportunities are more often chosen in a qualitative or subjective manner.

Figure 4.1	Rating Scale for Risks	
RISKS		
Severity	**Likelihood**	
1 = No potential for harm	1 = Very unlikely	
2 = Distraction/limited effect	2 = Possible, but not likely	
3 = Negative effect on sales and reputation	3 = Quite possible	
4 = Loss of major customers/ significant drop in revenue	4 = Likely	
5 = Death to employees/business closure	5 = Very likely	

The two rating factors shown in figure 4.1 (severity and likelihood) are multiplied to give you a risk priority number (RPN). Once you have rated the risks and opportunities and calculated the RPN for each one, select a threshold for action. For example, it might be all risks and opportunities whose RPNs are 10 or higher. All risks that fall into that category will be addressed through actions you determine. In this way, you're using your resources in the most efficient manner possible by acting on the most significant risks and opportunities.

6.1.2 (No subclause title)

Actions to address these risks and opportunities

ISO 9001:2015 tells you to plan actions to address risks and opportunities. These leaves a lot to your discretion. Your actions can be simple or elaborate, short term or long term, costly or cheap. How you address the risks and opportunities is up to you. There are three requirements:

- *They are planned.* You don't just come up with actions on the fly. You plan them. You carefully define what will happen, who will be involved, when it will be done, and what resources will be needed, as applicable.
- *They are integrated into QMS processes.* All the controls of the QMS will be applied to the actions. For instance, if they are maintained as documented information, then document control will apply. If measuring instruments are used, then calibration requirements will most likely apply.
- *They must be proportional.* The most significant risks will be matched with the most significant actions. Opportunities with the biggest payback will be matched with robust plans.
- *They are checked for effectiveness.* Once you implement your actions, you're not finished. You must determine if they achieved their objectives. Be as objective as possible when evaluating effectiveness.

ISO 9001:2015 doesn't require that your risks and opportunities be retained or maintained as documented information. However, we've already established that this is an important, foundational requirement of the standard. Are you going to leave something like this to tribal knowledge? Of course not.

Smart organizations will document their process for determining and rating risks and opportunities, and they will keep records of what they learn.

Risks and opportunities has the most interactions of any section of ISO 9001:2015. It's like an octopus with eight arms leading in every direction. To properly implement this section, you need to clearly understand how it connects to other parts of the standard. Here are the linkages:

- *4.1, Understanding the organization and its context.* This is possibly the single biggest input to your risks and opportunities. Much of what you learn in clause 4.1 can be copied over word-for-word. The internal and external issues that make up your organization's context are comprised largely of risks and opportunities, so make sure to do a deep dive into context.

- *4.2, Understanding the needs and expectations of interested parties.* Another key input to risks and opportunities are what your customers, suppliers, employees, regulators, and other interested parties require of you.

- *10.2.1(e), Corrective action.* When you fix something through corrective action, you have reduced risk. This makes it a periodic input to your risks and opportunities.

- *9.1.3(e), Analysis and evaluation.* This is both an input and an output of risk. You must evaluate the effectiveness of actions taken to address risks and opportunities, and what you learn from this evaluation will be reflected back as possible changes to your actions.

- *9.3.2(e), Management review.* Also an input and an output of risk. An input to management review is an evaluation of the effectiveness of actions taken to address risks and opportunities. This is almost an exact repeat of the requirement we just discussed in subclause 9.1.3(e). Handle this in management review, and you'll have addressed it in both places.

- *5.1.1(d), Leadership.* This is an output of risks and opportunity. Top management will promote risk-based thinking, and this will certainly involve a discussion of what the organization has identified as its risks.

- *5.1.2(d), Customer focus.* Another output of risks and opportunities. You're required to specifically determine risks and opportunities relating to product conformity and customer satisfaction.

- *4.4.1(f), QMS processes.* When you determine your QMS processes in 4.4.1(f), you also have to address the risks and opportunities that are applicable to those processes.

Most of these connections are just statements that equate to "Make sure you act on your risks and opportunities." Don't sweat all these connections.

It's important to note that the writers of ISO 9001:2015 intended there to be a connection between the opportunities that are part of risks and opportunities and the improvements that the organization takes action on in clause 10.1, Improvement—General. This relationship isn't spelled out very clearly, but it's a relationship that you should consider as you implement these requirements.

6.1 FREQUENTLY ASKED QUESTIONS

Do we have to use ISO 31000 or ISO 31010 when addressing risks and opportunities?

No, you're not required to use these guidance documents on risk management, but they might be helpful.

We chose to identify risks and opportunities directly related to our QMS. We didn't include risks related to safety or the environment. Is that OK?

Yes. ISO 9001:2015 states that the risks and opportunities you identify are those needed to give assurance that the QMS can achieve intended results. Since safety and environment are not specifically addressed by the QMS, you don't need to include them. I believe there are benefits to addressing risks in a universal manner, but that decision is yours.

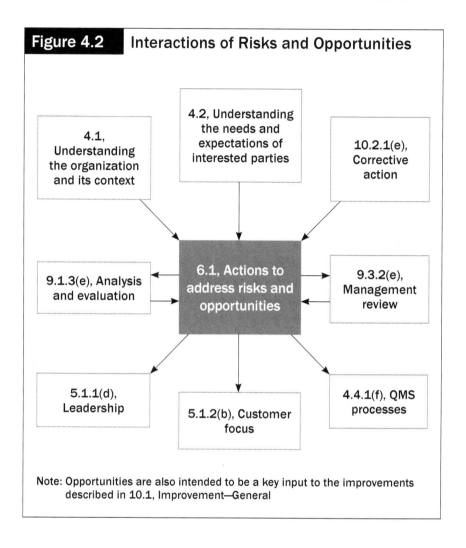

Figure 4.2   Interactions of Risks and Opportunities

Note: Opportunities are also intended to be a key input to the improvements described in 10.1, Improvement—General

The risk matrix shown in figure 4.3 provides an example of what this might look like. The example was developed for an organization that teaches onsite professional courses.

Figure 4.3   Risk Matrix Example

Buzz Quality Courses LLC

Risks related to teaching courses	Effect	Severity	Likelihood	RPN	Actions planned
Temperature problems in training room	Students complain	2.5	3	7.5	Ask about training room ahead of time; let students know they might want to bring a sweater.
Teams work at vastly different paces during exercises	Idle time; boredom; students lose interest	2.5	3	7.5	Carefully observe progress; possibly switch team members; try to choose balanced teams.
Cancellation of course after purchase of airline ticket	Loss of up to $1,000	3.5	2	7	Buy refundable airline tickets; ask company to purchase ticket on my behalf.
Computer won't connect to projector	Students can't see slides	2.5	2.5	6.25	Verify that IT support is available.
No snacks in room	Students hungry and irritated	2.5	2.5	6.25	Make sure that host knows what is needed, and that they agree to provide.
Students spend time on electronic devices during class	No class energy; course getting bogged down	2	3	6	Mention at the beginning of class to refrain from excessive device usage; let host know also.
Distractions from work (calls, emails, texts, visits)	No class energy; course getting bogged down	2	3	6	Mention at the beginning of class to avoid distractions and stay focused; let host know also.
Disruptive student/student with excessive questions	Spending too much time on one student	3	2	6	Be as accommodating as possible, but take excessive questions offline.
Disinterested students/unwilling participants	No class energy; course gets bogged down	3	2	6	Maintain high class energy; ask host to not include people who don't want to be there.
Tired instructor	Course lacks energy; students lose interest	2	3	6	Go to bed by midnight the night before.

Figure 4.3 Risk Matrix Example (Cont.)

Buzz Quality Courses LLC

Risks related to teaching courses	Effect	Severity	Likelihood	RPN	Actions planned
Course notebooks didn't arrive	Unprofessional appearance; confusion	3	2	6	Order notebooks one week before course; always use Mimeo.com for printing.
Course exercise falls apart	Unprofessional appearance; students lose interest	3	2	6	Beta test all exercises before including them; carefully monitor exercise progress.
Course materials too generic	Students not engaged	2	3	6	Customize course exercises (especially case details and props) to fit company/industry.
No coffee in room	Students groggy and irritated	2.5	2	5	Make sure host knows what is needed, and that they agree to provide.
Exercises not challenging enough	Students get bored and lose interest	2	2.5	5	Design exercises to be challenging; beta test all exercises before including them.
Nonpayment of invoice	Loss of $4,000–$10,000 depending on course	4	1	4	Get official purchase order issued before doing class; reference purchase order on invoice.
Breaks take too long	Course falls behind schedule; students lose interest	2	2	4	Give clear end time of breaks; round up students at end of break time.
Lunch takes too long	Course falls behind schedule; students lose interest	2	2	4	Give clear end time of lunch; round up students at end of lunch.
Projected slides don't match notebook	Confusion; unprofessional appearance	2	2	4	Maintain document control of materials; verify revision level before printing.
Course lacks warmth/too stiff	Students not engaged; feel alienated	2	2	4	Learn and use names of all students; incorporate humor throughout; encourage laughter.

6.2 QUALITY OBJECTIVES AND PLANNING TO ACHIEVE THEM

Equivalent to subclause 5.4.1 of ISO 9001:2008, with the addition of plans to achieve objectives.

Quality objectives have long been a part of ISO 9001. What's new in ISO 9001:2015 is the requirement for plans to achieve them. It's no longer enough to document the objectives, ensure that they're measurable, and tell employees about them. The organization must lay out a path for how it hopes to achieve the objectives. These plans must describe what actions will be performed, what resources will be required, who will be involved, the time frames for completion, and metrics for success. This is a much more meaningful approach to implementing objectives, but it will require a bit more proactivity on the part of the organization.

It might be helpful to describe what we mean by "quality objectives." Quality objectives are measurable goals that relate to your organization's commitments to quality. Quality is a very broad topic. ISO 9000:2015 defines "quality" as the degree to which an object's characteristics meets requirements. ISO 9000:2015 further defines an "object" as anything perceivable or conceivable. This opens up the world of quality objectives to just about anything that matters to the organization's success. As a result, objectives can address a wide range of topics: product conformance, process performance, customer satisfaction, workplace safety, financial results, market share, cost reduction, and many others. When reviewing objectives that aren't traditional quality measures, I have heard auditors utter the comment, "These quality objectives aren't sufficiently related to quality." This is ridiculous. As long as quality objectives measure the degree to which characteristics conform to requirements, they are fine.

There is a good argument for not even using the term "quality objectives." The term can mislead personnel into thinking that these metrics can only address topics related to quality control or quality assurance. As we've already discussed, quality objectives can relate to almost anything that bears on the organization's success. If a different name reinforces that point, then by all means substitute the term "quality objectives" with a different name. Good alternatives include business objectives, scorecard goals, key measures, and performance targets. There is nothing in ISO 9001:2015 that says you must use the same terminology as the standard. In fact, ISO 9001:2015 is full of terminology that could be better understood by using more straightforward language.

As the organization thinks about quality objectives, it should consider what's already being measured. There is a strong chance that current goals and objectives are being measured because they're important. This sounds silly, but it's worth mentioning. Organizations have a bad habit of trying to reinvent the wheel when it comes to objectives. If you already know what drives success in your organization—and you're already measuring it—then those measures should be your quality objectives. Top management should be fully engaged in the choice. Their involvement will help reinforce true drivers of success. Do not let the term "quality objectives" sway you from what you should be measuring.

6.2.1 (No subclause title)

ISO 9001:2015 uses the plural form of objectives. That means there must be more than one. But how many should an organization shoot for? There is no right answer to this question, but you should keep in mind that the purpose of objectives is to tell everybody what's important to the organization. Objectives keep people focused. They should separate the message from the noise. By understanding the quality objectives, employees know which direction the organization is headed and how they contribute to that direction. If you have too many objectives, the focus is lost and you're back to confusion. Four to eight objectives are usually adequate. This number enables the organization to address a variety of important concerns, yet keep the list nice and tight.

Let's examine the specific requirements related to objectives in ISO 9001:2015:

- *Established throughout the organization.* What exactly does it mean when ISO 9001 says that quality objectives must be established at relevant functions and levels? I'll clear it up for you very quickly. Everyone who's irrelevant raise your hand. What, no hands? Does that mean that everyone plays a role in providing the organization's products, at least at some level? The answer is yes. All organizations are composed of a supply chain of internal functions, all working together. Any break in that supply chain affects the organization's ability to provide its products. Thus, all functions and levels are relevant.

That said, everyone within the scope of the management system will have quality objectives. These will either be organizationwide objectives that apply to everyone or functional objectives that specifically address departmental responsibilities and output. Objectives can even be a mix of both. However, no one can plausibly claim that there aren't any objectives that apply to them. Your quality objectives will touch everybody in the organization in some manner, and everybody will have the ability to contribute to their achievement.

This means that everybody who is relevant to the organization will have at least one objective that applies to him or her. "Relevant" means that your work is essential to the organization. Whose work isn't essential to the organization? If someone has been hired to do a task, it should be essential to the organization or the person wouldn't be in the position. The "relevance" requirement means that the organization should choose broad, strategic objectives that apply to as many people and processes as possible. That doesn't mean that certain topics shouldn't be pinpointed, especially if they have great importance. It means that unless you want a hundred objectives, some of them should be fairly broad and universal.

- *Supporting the quality policy.* The quality policy is the uppermost document within your QMS. It sets the tone for everything else that comes underneath it. You might even call it the mother document. Quality objectives must be aligned with its themes. Any special claims or commitments the organization includes in its quality policy must be backed up by objectives. You can't just make a statement in the quality policy and expect the words to magically transform the organization; you've got to develop an objective that will illustrate your success or failure. Carefully examine your quality policy and make sure that anything above and beyond the minimum commitments required by ISO 9001 is supported by an objective.

Years ago I worked for a company that put this statement into its quality policy: "We are committed to long-term partnerships with our customers and suppliers." An auditor rightfully asked the question, "Do you have any objectives relating to long-term partnerships?" Of course we didn't. Nobody had interpreted the requirement literally, which is exactly the way it should be interpreted.

- *Objectives must be quantifiable.* This point is very simple, but it bears explanation. An organization's quality objectives must be measurable and they must define exactly how the desired state will be achieved. General themes, philosophies, and aspirations rarely constitute measurable objectives. Although ISO 9001's guidelines are quite straightforward, vague objectives abound, such as:
  - ✓ Incorporate excellence into all we do.
  - ✓ Offer a challenging and rewarding environment for our employees.
  - ✓ Earn the respect of our neighbors in the community.
  - ✓ Create an unmatched service experience for all our customers.
  - ✓ Make associates proud they joined our team.

  Despite being admirable concepts, these aren't measurable objectives. However, they could serve as possible first steps toward measurable objectives. The trick is to look at lofty aspirations and ask, "What indicates whether we've done that or not?" Keep asking that question until you uncover a metric that gets to the heart of success or failure. Get specific about what you're trying to achieve. Platitudes such as "Incorporate excellence into all we do" are so vague that they serve no purpose.

  The main reason for setting measurable objectives has nothing to do with ISO 9001 and everything to do with becoming more successful. People have trouble contributing to fuzzy, undefined objectives. They can't tell whether their efforts are making a difference because the objective can't be gauged. As a consequence, the organization begins to drift like a rudderless boat. However, measurable objectives focus everyone's energies and creative powers. Combined with leadership and an empowered work force, measurable objectives pave the way to success.

- *Consider applicable requirements.* This is an extremely broad requirement that requires some clarification. Who provides the clarification? You do. It's up to the organization to define what requirements apply to it. If any of these requirements are especially critical to your success, you'll establish objectives related to them. Some of these requirements might be written into your quality policy, but others won't be. Examine what you learned in clause 4.1, Understanding the organization and its context, and in 4.2, Understanding the needs and expectations of interested parties, and these should point you toward some requirements that could be included within your quality objectives.

- *Be appropriate for effective products and services and customer satisfaction.* This means that your objectives have to have an effect on two important concepts: product and service conformity, and customer satisfaction. Demonstration of this would be especially easy if you simply included at least one objective that related to your product. Obvious candidates include:
  - ✓ Inspection results
  - ✓ Product reliability
  - ✓ Service effectiveness
  - ✓ On-time delivery performance
  - ✓ Warranty returns
  - ✓ Jobs completed according to plan
  - ✓ Services requiring rework

  The reality is that any meaningful objectives will have at least some connection to your products and your customers. As long as there is a logical connection and you can explain the connection, nobody can take issue with what you've decided to measure.

- *Be checked on a routine basis.* These are simple words, but they're powerful in what they require. Set your objectives, and then monitor how you're doing against them. Believe it or not, this is a new requirement in ISO 9001:2015. Previous versions of the standard didn't explicitly require you to monitor your objectives. The requirement for monitoring is firmly established, so it's helpful to answer a few key questions:
  - ✓ How often are objectives monitored?
  - ✓ Who is responsible for gathering the data?
  - ✓ Are any calculations necessary, and if so, what are they?
  - ✓ How is progress against objectives displayed or depicted?

✓ Who is responsible for analyzing the objectives and drawing conclusions?

✓ Are the plans for achieving objectives also monitored?

If you see a logical connection between the monitoring of objectives and management review, then you're headed in the right direction. Top management should be a leader in monitoring and analyzing objectives. Management review is the perfect forum. One of the new inputs to management review is "the extent to which quality objectives have been met," so this makes the connection perfectly clear.

- *Be shared and discussed.* At their heart, quality objectives are nothing more than communication tools. Their purpose is to tell employees what measures are most important to your success. So make sure to share the message as often as possible. Any gathering of employees, whether actual or virtual, is a good time to remind employees about the objectives. All organizational communications are fair game, also. These include leadership emails, newsletters, bulletin board postings, intranet updates, and any other transmission of information. Keep in mind that some employees may not be in the habit of thinking about corporate goals. Get them in the habit! Answers to these questions should be part of any communications plan:

  ✓ What exactly are our objectives? Yes, remind them for the hundredth time.

  ✓ Why are they important? Explain why these objectives matter and why achieving them will make a difference to the organization.

  ✓ What specifically can employees do in each process to contribute? Be very specific. Provide guides to action to get employees thinking.

- *Be revised as often as needed.* Nothing remains static in business. The competitive landscape changes constantly, sometimes on a daily basis. Objectives must change to reflect new realities. For instance, revenue growth might have been critical two years ago, but now it's more important for the organization to generate a profit—two different objectives with different means to achieve them. Don't let your objectives become static measures. Achieving objectives should become a companywide goal, but the objectives themselves must be adaptable. They'll evolve to reflect changes in strategy, the environment, and your customers' needs. It's reasonable to expect that your quality objectives will be revised at least once a year.

- *Document your quality objectives.* This means your objectives must be written down in a document. In the current verbiage of ISO 9001:2015, the objectives will be "maintained as documented information." The document will typically be fairly short, usually a page or two at the most. Like all documents, it will be approved and be controlled for revision. Some organizations elect to combine their quality objectives with other documents. I have even seen the quality objectives and quality policy combined on more than one occasion. Do it in whatever way makes sense, just make sure that your objectives are documented.

6.2.2 (No subclause title)

The second half of the section on quality objectives addresses the plans for achieving them. Each objective must be matched to an improvement plan. Because every objective is different, it stands to reason that every plan will be different. Your plans should answer each of the following questions:

- *What actions will be taken on objectives?* You must be specific. Saying, "By trying harder" isn't specific enough. What processes will be changed? How are they going to be changed? What intermediate steps will be taken? Lay out the actions in a logical manner so they can be implemented.
- *What resources will be needed to carry out actions?* Change requires resources. These might include funds, time, people, facilities, equipment, and/or information. Document the necessary resources, then make sure they're available before trying to implement the plan.
- *Who will take the actions?* Who's responsible for each step of the plan? Clearly designate and communicate responsibilities and hold people accountable. Don't leave anything to chance.
- *When will actions be finished?* Plans for establishing objectives take time to implement. How much time do you think you'll need? Your time frames must be documented, especially when multiple steps are linked.

- *How will you determine the effectiveness of the actions?* The most logical place to evaluate results is within management review. You already have top management, data inputs, and momentum for analysis. This doesn't mean that evaluation of actions is limited to management review, but it's the best forum for maximum visibility and engagement of leadership.

ISO 9001:2015 does not specifically say that plans for achieving objectives are maintained within documented information. How else could you communicate and implement your plans, though? Document your plans for achieving objectives and make sure the information is shared widely. An example is shown below:

Example Quality Objectives

Objective 1: Maintain zero lost-time accidents

Action 1:

- *What will be done:* Hold regular safety meetings to discuss hazards and near misses
- *Resources required:* 15 minutes, training room
- *Who's responsible:* Department manager
- *When to be completed:* Weekly on Thursdays at 9:00 a.m.
- *How results evaluated:* Verify that meetings are held in every department. Also track near misses and lost-time accidents.

Objective 2: Perform new job set-ups in 20 minutes or less

Action 2:

- *What will be done:* Create a pre-set-up of the upcoming job while the current job is still running. Use the "pre-set-up template" to ensure a mirror image of the actual set-up as it will run.
- *Resources required:* Pre-set-up template, rolling tool box, set-up specifications

- *Who's responsible:* Set-up supervisor
- *When to be completed:* Fully implement pre-set-ups on all machines by Sept. 1, 20XX
- *How results evaluated:* Record the start time and end time of each set-up, using the Job Tracker system. Graph results on each machine and display on production board.

Objective 3: Reduce dimensional defects to less than 1 percent of all finished products

Action 3:

- *What will be done:* Institute first-piece inspections at the start of each new production run. Also, inspect dies for visual and dimensional defects prior to installation.
- *Resources required:* First-piece inspection reports, calipers, die inspection reports
- *Who's responsible:* Operators
- *When to be completed:* Prior to each production run. To be fully implemented by Sept. 15, 20XX
- *How results evaluated:* Verification of all first-piece inspections and die inspections being done. Tracking of dimensional defects on a weekly basis as a percentage of all production. Results graphed and posted in the production area.

6.2 FREQUENTLY ASKED QUESTIONS

I understand that ISO 9001:2015 requires quality objectives to be documented, but do the plans for achieving them also have to be documented?

Yes, I would interpret the documentation requirement as applying to the quality objectives and to the plans for achieving them. Document both.

6.2 FREQUENTLY ASKED QUESTIONS

Everyone in our organization has his or her own personal objectives. Does this satisfy ISO 9001:2015 requirements?

Maybe. The intent of this requirement is to determine organizational objectives, not personal objectives. Make sure that you have established objectives on a broader scale (organizational, functional, or departmental). Personal objectives may then stem from the higher level objectives, if that's the way your organization wants to operate.

Can we include our quality objectives in our quality policy?

You can if you want, but it makes more sense to maintain them as separate documents. The objectives are likely to change much more often than the policy.

Can we use profit as a quality objective? Our consultant told us we can't because it has nothing to do with quality.

Yes, you can use profit as a quality objective. Quality is a very broad topic and can encompass nearly anything the organization does. Profit certainly reflects on the quality of your processes and products.

6.3 PLANNING OF CHANGES

Somewhat equivalent to subclause 5.4.2 of ISO 9001:2008, but with many additional requirements.

Change will happen to you and your organization. The question is this: Are you going to manage the change or allow yourself to be overwhelmed by it? The only path to survival is to get ahead of the curve and address change systematically: Define the change, study the effects, and identify the interactions. Like so many of the new requirements in ISO 9001:2015, this section could be summarized by the motto of "Be proactive." In truth, this requirement isn't entirely new. There was a subclause that flirted with change management in ISO 9001:2008 (5.4.2), but it didn't require the organization to do much.

Change management is a fully realized concept in ISO 9001:2015. This clause specifically addresses planned changes. Examples of these sorts of events could include:

- Purchase of new equipment
- Hiring of additional employees
- Adoption of new methods or tools
- Significant change in raw materials or supplies
- Application of new regulatory rules

Although any change you make should be planned and deliberate, ISO 9001:2015 focuses on significant changes. Minor tweaks to your operation will happen all the time. If you went through a change management process every time you made a tweak, you'd never get any work done. The standard asks you to consider significant changes that could hurt you if they weren't managed properly. This is really a judgment call on the part of your leadership team to decide what changes must go through a change management process. Just be able to rationally explain why certain changes did or did not go through change management.

ISO 9000:2015 defines "change management" as addressing four distinct elements: the purpose of the change and its consequences, integrity of the QMS, availability of resources, and responsibilities and authorities. Let's discuss each of these:

- *Consider changes and their possible ramifications.* The first step is to understand the changes and why you're making them. These two pieces of information are usually well understood. What is not as well understood is the third element required by ISO 9001:2015: the potential consequences or ramifications of the change. Consequences can be positive or negative. Just as you've done for other requirements in this standard, you're speculating on what might happen. ISO 9001:2015 doesn't require that this be documented, but it would be virtually worthless if you didn't document it. Make sure to document the following details:
  - ✓ The change to be made
  - ✓ The purpose of the change
  - ✓ Potential consequences of the change

Use a form of some kind, either hard copy or electronic, that captures these issues and guides you through change management. Keep it simple and concise so that employees won't mind utilizing it when necessary.

- *Consider how the QMS will be maintained during change.* Despite all the work that people put into implementing the QMS, the system gets forgotten regularly. ISO 9001:2015 tells you not to forget your system when making changes. What parts of the system will be affected by the change? Some typical QMS considerations include:
  - ✓ *Maintained documentation.* Do we need to write a procedure that describes the change or revise an existing procedure?
  - ✓ *Retained documentation.* Do we need to establish any new record-keeping as a result of the change?
  - ✓ *Training.* Do our employees need training to understand the change?
  - ✓ *Objectives.* Should we revisit our goals and objectives as a result of the change?
  - ✓ *Infrastructure.* Do we need to institute maintenance as a result of the change, or revise existing maintenance schedules?
  - ✓ *Monitoring and measurement.* Will the change require new inspection processes? Will new measuring instruments be required?

  There's no requirement that you consider every single aspect of your QMS, but make sure to hit the key ones. The point is to ensure that your QMS assists and facilitates the change, instead of playing catch-up later. If you've established a form to retain information about each change, make a note of how your QMS will be affected and how you intend to utilize your QMS to successfully implement it.

- *Consider resources that will be needed for the change.* Few things in life happen without resources, especially change within organizations. Changes may require time, money, tools, equipment, people, space, and the like. If you want your change to be implemented successfully, you'll proactively determine what resources you'll need. Resources actually require two elements for effective planning:
  - ✓ The resources needed, with a clear description of any applicable specifications

✓   How the resource will be obtained

- *Consider responsibilities and authorities related to the change.* Change must be owned by someone. The organization must define who has responsibility for each change, and who has authority. In other words, who must do something, and who can do something. Clear accountability through responsibilities and authorities will help ensure the change is implemented as expected. It would also be helpful to think about how existing responsibilities and authorities might need to be revised due to the planned change.

ISO 9001:2015 doesn't explicitly require maintained information (e.g., a procedure) for change management, but I would strongly recommend it. The standard also doesn't require retained information (i.e., records) of having planned and managed changes, but it would be almost impossible to provide evidence of performing change management without records of some sort.

6.3 FREQUENTLY ASKED QUESTIONS

We have established a change management process, but we're not clear on scope. Does every change we make have to be run through it?

No, of course not. Within your change management process, you should establish criteria for the types of changes that will be considered. Only changes above a certain level (such as a dollar amount, number of people affected, connection to products, or connection to customers) would go through your change management process. I would also keep your process as streamlined and practical as possible. That way, it's not burdensome.

6.3 FREQUENTLY ASKED QUESTIONS

Do we have to keep records of changes and how they were planned?

ISO 9001:2015 doesn't require records (i.e., retained documented information), but it will be more difficult to prove that changes happened without records. Also, the process will be more consistent and effective if it is guided by a form or documented procedure. But you aren't required to keep records or have a documented procedure.

Chapter 5

ISO 9001:2015 Section 7 Support

7.1 RESOURCES

7.1.1 General

Equivalent to clause 6.1 of ISO 9001:2008.

This is a very short section of ISO 9001:2015, which acts as a preview to the more in-depth requirements on resources. It asks you to determine resources necessary for the quality management system (QMS). Because this is such a generalized and high-level requirement, most organizations can skip it and focus on the remainder of the more detailed requirements in clause 7.1. If you wanted to address it specifically, such a high-level requirement is best matched with a high-level solution. Any sort of budgeting or planning process, typically conducted on an annual basis and led by top management, will satisfy this requirement. Just make sure that the budgeting or planning process specifically addresses some of the aspects of the QMS.

Examples include resources needed for any of the following:

- Internal auditing
- Training
- Communication
- Calibration

- Maintenance
- Software used with the QMS

ISO 9001:2015 further mentions that the organization should consider:
- Existing internal resources
- External providers

This simply means that you should designate where the resources will come from. This obviously affects the cost and timing of the resources, so it's likely to be addressed in the budget or business plan as a practical matter.

7.1.2 People

Equivalent to clause 6.2 in ISO 9001:2008.

One-sentence requirements in ISO 9001 have always been a source of mystery. Is the requirement so short because it perfectly addresses the essence of its topic, or is it so short because the requirement is simply a theme that is examined in much better detail later in the standard? In the present case, ISO 9001:2015 provides a very high-level requirement on people. It states that the organization will determine and provide the people needed for its QMS and the operation of its processes. Do you have people in your organization? Yes. Are they needed for your QMS and your processes? Yes. Answering "yes" to both questions means you have met this requirement. The only cases where an organization might fail to meet this requirement would be if it's short-staffed or employs the wrong mix of people. People are addressed in more meaningful and actionable ways in clauses 7.1.6, Organizational knowledge; 7.2, Competence; 7.3, Awareness; and 7.4, Communication.

7.1.3 Infrastructure

Equivalent to clause 6.3 in ISO 9001:2008.

An organization's infrastructure is made up of the physical assets that enable it to produce. The specific assets will vary considerably, depending on the nature of its products. Here are some examples based on a few different types of organizations:

- *Delivery company.* This type of firm relies heavily on assets that move product and store it securely. Thus, its critical infrastructure consists of trucks and warehouse facilities. The trucks are maintained under a service contract with a fleet maintenance company, and the warehouses are maintained by the real estate company they are leased from. As such, all maintenance is outsourced, but the effectiveness of maintenance is monitored on a regular basis. Any maintenance problems are reported to the outsourcing company and the organization is required to take corrective action. The company does an annual review of its maintenance providers and decides whether to continue its maintenance contracts.

- *Investment firm.* This firm relies heavily on infrastructure that provides and stores information. In other words, information technology (IT) is critical to its success. The firm has an IT department that maintains its computer hardware, software, and virus protection. There is also an IT trouble ticket process for users to report problems that require special attention. The IT department measures its effectiveness on how quickly it responds to maintenance needs.

- *Manufacturing plant.* This organization uses large industrial equipment to produce its products. Each piece of equipment has a monthly, quarterly, and yearly maintenance program. The maintenance is scheduled so that equipment downtime is minimized, so the plant exercises some discretion in its exact timing. The majority of the maintenance is performed by a centralized maintenance department, but some daily maintenance is performed by production personnel prior to beginning their work each day. The production and maintenance departments meet weekly to discuss the timing and effectiveness of maintenance and to revise maintenance schedules as needed.

Identify needed infrastructure and make it available

ISO 9001:2015 provides some of its own examples of infrastructure in the notes section at the end of subclause 7.1.3. It lists such assets as buildings, utilities, equipment, hardware, software, transport, and communication. As we've discussed, not all these assets are created equally. It's the responsibility of each organization to determine what its product-critical infrastructure consists of. ISO 9001:2015 requires that the organization determine and provide the infrastructure needed to operate its processes and achieve conformity of products and services. The key words are "operate processes" and "achieve conformity of products and services." Whatever helps you do this is what you need to focus on from an infrastructure standpoint.

If your organization is producing products and satisfying customers, it has already determined and provided infrastructure. The physical assets have already been acquired, at least on an initial basis. Determining and providing infrastructure isn't a one-time activity. It's something that must be revisited periodically as customers, products, and personnel change. Management review is a good opportunity to consider changes in infrastructure, as are strategic planning sessions, budgeting activities, and staff meetings. ISO 9001:2015 doesn't require that you keep records of determining and providing resources, only that you do it. The more discipline you can build around infrastructure, though, the fewer operational problems you'll have.

Maintain infrastructure

ISO 9001:2015 simply requires that your infrastructure be maintained. It doesn't require that you do this yourself, and it doesn't specify any frequencies or methods for maintenance. The entire program is up to you to design. As long as there is some sort of maintenance routine in place and there is evidence that it's effective, nobody has any right to challenge it.

You aren't required to maintain documented information of your maintenance program or schedules, but it would be a good idea to ensure that everyone is on the same page. Likewise, retained information (i.e., records) are not explicitly required, but it would be difficult to prove that you're following your program without records. Strongly consider documenting your maintenance program and keeping records of fulfilling its requirements.

Just as the determination of infrastructure is not a one-time activity, the design of the maintenance program must be periodically revisited. The timing of maintenance, specific activities, and competence of maintenance personnel are likely to change periodically. Make the effectiveness of your maintenance process one of your measurable objectives and monitor it. Exactly what the objective is will obviously differ, depending on the type of maintenance being performed and the requirements that the organization has set.

Preventive and predictive maintenance

ISO 9001:2015 doesn't require, or even mention, preventive or predictive maintenance. It simply requires maintenance, period. The specific type of maintenance program you implement is up to you. Common sense dictates that preventive and predictive maintenance are good ideas. They lower the overall costs of maintenance and increase the availability and productivity of equipment. Should you decide to implement a more robust approach to maintenance, that's the system against which you will be audited within the scope of your management system. Don't let this discourage you from doing what makes sense for your business.

7.1.3 FREQUENTLY ASKED QUESTIONS

Our organization is located in a rented office. The landlord takes care of all maintenance. What should we do about the infrastructure requirements of ISO 9001:2015?

In the case of an office environment, the office building is likely to be less important than the equipment within the building. Focus on things like the computer system, telephones, and other infrastructure that are needed to produce your products within the office environment. Also make sure you have communicated your building requirements to the landlord.

7.1.4 Environment for the operation of processes

Equivalent to clause 6.4 of ISO 9001:2008.

An organization's environment is made up of the conditions that exist in its workplace. The conditions required by ISO 9001:2015 refer to its processes, and those required to achieve conformity of product and services. Examples of environmental conditions include configuration of the work area, employee health and safety, lighting, temperature, humidity, noise, vibration, cleanliness, pest control, and contamination. The required work environment will vary greatly, depending on the product. Consider the following examples:

- *Candy manufacturer.* Raw materials are received into the facility and immediately moved into a climate-controlled storage area. The cleanliness of the storage area is immaculate. A weekly inspection is conducted to look for any evidence of pests. Raw materials are transported into the manufacturing area by personnel wearing white gloves and smocks, and all manufacturing is tightly controlled under good manufacturing practices. All outside doors and windows are kept closed and the housekeeping is very strict; even the garbage cans are spotless. Nobody with any kind of illness is permitted inside the facility, and no jewelry is permitted. Once manufacturing is complete, the finished product is stored in an area that is maintained at 40° F, +/- 4°, and the gage used to monitor the temperature is calibrated. A weekly audit is conducted to evaluate the condition of finished product in inventory.

- *Insurance company.* People are stationed at desks and perform work on computers and telephones. The office temperature is maintained at typical office conditions, which is usually a compromise between the women who like the office warmer and the men who like it cooler. Dress codes are enforced so personnel are not distracted in their work and to maintain a professional environment in the event customers visit. Personnel are not allowed to play music from their radios or computers, as the sound disturbs people in their work, even when played at low volume. Hot food items are restricted to the break rooms, as some employees were offended by the smells of certain foods that were consumed at desks. Personal photographs and decorations are permitted in cubicles, but nothing that could constitute a threatening work environment is allowed. Everything about the office is maintained in a pleasant yet bland manner because this is the environment that was found to result in the highest productivity, lowest service defects, and fewest personnel problems.

- *Paper mill.* The inside of the plant is very damp, and a half-inch of water is on most of the floors. Additionally, the nature of the production process is very hot in some areas, and the ambient temperature in the summer can reach more than 110° F. During winter months, temperatures in the warehouses are just a few degrees above freezing. For many years, the harsh environmental conditions were simply accepted as a given. The conditions didn't negatively affect the product, so management felt no need to change anything. Recently, it became clear that employees were becoming ill at a higher than normal rate, however. The increased illnesses affected the mill's attendance rate, which in turn affected its ability to produce paper on schedule. Work conditions are being improved now that the link between the environment and product conformity was recognized.

In all these cases, the environment is focused on what is needed for the product the organization produces and the processes that make it happen. Sometimes organizations discover connections between the environment and product conformity that they didn't know existed, as in the paper mill example. ISO 9001:2015 simply says that you will determine the environmental conditions that you require. Whatever you require is what you will be expected to provide and maintain.

Here are some typical controls related to specific work environment variables:

- *Temperature and humidity.* Gages for monitoring, records of conditions, records of gage calibration, investigation of affected product when conditions fail to meet environmental requirements
- *Safety hazards.* Identification of hazards, prioritization of risks, procedures for job safety, monitoring of compliance, records of monitoring, corrective action on accidents and near misses, regular meetings to discuss safety issues
- *Lighting, noise, vibration.* Specifications for characteristics, procedures for maintaining specifications, ongoing measurement of characteristics, records of measurement, calibration of gages, records of calibration
- *Housekeeping.* Procedures for housekeeping, defined responsibilities, training of personnel, periodic audits of housekeeping, corrective action on nonconformities, signage to remind personnel of guidelines
- *Personal hygiene and behavior.* Documented policies for personnel, recurring training, monitoring by supervisors, and counseling for employees

ISO 9001:2015 doesn't require that you maintain or retain documented information (procedures or records) related to environment, though it usually makes sense to have them in place. In cases where the organization establishes requirements for environment, the only way to verify that the environmental conditions were met would be through records. Documentation would also be required to consistently communicate environmental requirements and controls.

The notes section at the end of subclause 7.1.4 expand what people might consider to be the environment, including social, psychological, and physical factors. Social, in particular, seems to stray far beyond what most people would consider to be the purview of the QMS. These are provided only as examples of what the organization might consider, not requirements that must be specifically addressed. The bottom line is that it's always up to the organization to determine the environmental characteristics that affect its processes, products, and services.

7.1.4 FREQUENTLY ASKED QUESTIONS

We have a gage that monitors the temperature of our warehouse, which must be maintained at 50° F +/- 10°. Does the gage have to be calibrated?

Yes. Because you've committed to a particular work environment, having accurate readings of that environment is necessary.

The note at the bottom of this section includes a lot of unusual environmental factors: social, psychological, physical. We don't have to consider all these, do we?

No, these are simply given as examples. It's very unlikely that many companies will take environment to those extremes, because the conditions needed for running processes and products don't require consideration.

7.1.5 Monitoring and measuring resources

7.1.5.1 General

Equivalent to clause 7.6 in ISO 9001:2008, but with less emphasis on calibration.

The focus of this section is determining the "suitability" and "fitness for purpose" of measuring instruments. This is a departure from previous revisions of ISO 9001, which focused almost entirely on calibration. Calibration may still be applied, but the organization now has much more discretion in how it determines suitability and fitness for purpose. The decision hinges on the need for measurement traceability. If traceability is required, then calibration or verification is triggered.

Let's back up and define a couple of key terms: suitability and fitness for purpose. Suitability means selecting the correct monitoring or measuring resource for the job at hand. The resource must be capable of making the measurements required and have enough resolution to detect the increments sought. For example, a floor scale used for weighing pallets of material is not suitable for detecting grams. The instrument simply wasn't designed to read in increments that small. Suitability comes into play when a monitoring or measuring resource is selected, and again as the organization's processes and products are modified. A particular resource might be suitable for some jobs but not others.

Fitness for purpose requires maintaining the monitoring or measuring resource in a way that preserves its ability to make measurements. This can encompass a wide variety of activities, including:

- Calibration
- Verification
- Preventive maintenance
- Breakdown maintenance and repair
- Visual inspection of the resource for damage or deterioration
- Automatic replacement after a defined timeframe
- Repeatability and reproducibility studies
- Statistical analysis of measurement variation

Calibration is the most typical process for ensuring fitness for purpose, but organizations have other choices. It's the organization's responsibility to analyze its monitoring and measuring resources, understand how they're used, and determine what process will best indicate fitness for purpose. Here are some examples:

- *Visual inspection.* The Western Novelty Company makes marketing displays for retail stores. The displays are made of cardboard and plastic, and have dimensional tolerances of +/- 0.25″. At this tolerance, the quality manager has determined that tape measures are suitable for the measurements to be made. To ensure fitness for purpose, the tape measures are visually inspected for damage by the quality technician twice a year. The quality technician ensures that the numbers and markers are clear, the tab on the end is intact, and there are no kinks, bends, or cuts in the tape. A record of the each tape measure's fitness for purpose is retained in the lab.

- *Automatic replacement.* R.M. Zimburger Inc. mills aluminum trihydrate powder for a variety of industrial applications. Each batch is tested in the lab using metal sieves with varying mesh sizes to test the particle size of the powder. The metal sieves are replaced every December to ensure they're fit for use. The manufacturer of sieves has warrantied that the sieves should remain accurate for at least two years unless they're dropped or punctured.

- *Verification.* Grandma's Catering provides breakfasts and lunches for local businesses. They deliver pre-prepared food in stainless steel serving trays, which are warmed by gel fuel cans. Mercury thermometers are used to ensure that the temperature of food is maintained at a minimum of 140° F. Twice a year the thermometers are verified by checking them in boiling water. As long as the thermometers read 212° F +/- 5° F they are considered verified. The owner of Grandma's Catering states that because they generally use the set point of 145° F for food (5° F above the temperature danger zone), the 5° F tolerance ensures that they are fit for use. Thermometers that fall outside the verification tolerance are replaced. The owner of Grandma's Catering maintains records of the thermometer verification.

ISO 9001:2015 requires that you retain documented information (i.e., records) on fitness for purpose. If you perform calibration, then naturally this would indicate fitness for purpose. As we've discussed, a handful of other activities might also indicate fitness for purpose. Whatever evidence proves fitness for purpose should be retained as a record. Also be prepared to explain why your method makes sense.

Where does monitoring and measurement take place?

One of your first tasks is determining where monitoring and measurement takes place. If you're not sure, take a full inventory. Here are some examples of monitoring and measurement:

- *Product.* You probably have multiple processes for verifying product conformity (and possibly service conformity). These processes may take place in a lab, quality control area, production department, or where a service is provided. When people think of monitoring and measuring resources, verifying product conformity is usually the first thing that comes to mind.

- *Process.* There are multiple processes within your organization that transform inputs into outputs. These processes are often monitored and measured to make sure they operate within specified parameters. Processes might be monitored for speed, accuracy, pressure, feed rate, or any other relevant characteristic.

- *Environment.* Locations within your organization may require special environmental conditions. These environmental conditions are monitored through measuring instruments and often relate to temperature, humidity, or cleanliness. Examples of locations include laboratories, product storage areas, and sensitive work areas.

- *Measuring instruments.* If you have measuring instruments, you may have standards for checking them. This checking may constitute calibration or may be a verification between calibrations. Regardless of what you call it, this is also a measurement process.

The requirements of subclause 7.1.5 are applied, at a minimum, to monitoring and measuring resources used to verify the conformity of products and services to requirements. If you're using measuring equipment to make sure your product or service meets requirements, be prepared to demonstrate its fitness for purpose.

7.1.5.2 Measurement traceability

The scope of calibration in ISO 9001:2015

In ISO 9001:2015, the requirements for calibration are triggered by the need for measurement traceability. If you or your customers require an unbroken chain of traceability back to a national or international standard, then you will need to calibrate your monitoring and measuring resources. If you need your resources to be accurate, calibration is the most logical process.

Calibration is far-and-away the most commonly used strategy for demonstrating fitness for purpose, so we will dedicate the majority of this section to the topic. Calibration is the act of measuring a standard of known quality with a measuring instrument and evaluating the difference between the standard and the actual instrument measurement. All measuring equipment has a calibration tolerance, which is typically a fraction of the measurement tolerances the instrument is used to verify. So, if the measuring instrument is used to measure a product tolerance of 10 mm +/- 1 mm, then the calibration tolerance might be 10 mm +/- 0.25 mm. If an instrument's measurements fall outside calibration tolerances, then it must be adjusted, repaired, or removed from use. It's important to note that measurement standards used during calibration are also measuring equipment that require periodic calibration.

Calibrate or verify

As we discussed, calibration involves measuring a standard of known quality with a measuring instrument and evaluating the difference between the known quality and the measurement from the instrument. Verification involves the same sort of checking as calibration, but it happens between calibrations. So, if an instrument gets calibrated every six months, we might verify it once a week. The point of verification is to detect small changes in an instrument's accuracy before it goes out of calibration.

At specified intervals

You must decide how often calibration and/or verification must take place. In the language of ISO 9001:2015, these are your "specified intervals." Manufacturers of measurement equipment often establish recommended calibration frequencies for their equipment. The recommended frequency is usually a good starting point for you to use. As you learn about the reliability of the equipment in your own environment, you're free to alter it. For example, if a manufacturer recommends that its scales be calibrated every 90 days, but you have two years of data showing that it only needs calibration every 180 days, then you're free to lengthen the interval. The key is backing up your decisions with data. This isn't an explicit requirement of ISO 9001:2015, but a requirement of rational decision making.

When an organization decides how often each piece of measuring equipment must be calibrated and/or verified, it usually documents this in a calibration schedule. This schedule can take the form of a list, schedule, file, binder, database, spreadsheet, or any number of other media. The objective is that you can easily determine when devices are coming due for calibration. There are numerous software applications that can serve as calibration scheduling aids. Regardless of how the information is stored, these are the most common bits of information retained for each measuring resource:

- Serial number
- Location
- Procedure used when calibrating
- Who carried out calibration (or ensured fitness for purpose)
- Last calibration date
- Next calibration date

Use traceable standards

Whatever standard you use for calibration must be traceable to an established source. In other words, you don't get to decide for yourself what makes a meter, a pound, or a gallon. You rely on a metrological source for these standard qualities. In the United States, the source for most standard measures is the National Institute of Standards and Technology (NIST). The standards used for calibration must have an unbroken chain of calibrations back to the source. You don't have to send your standards directly to NIST to be calibrated, but following the trail of what was used for calibration should lead us to NIST or another established source. It's expected that your certificates for calibration will indicate the standards used for calibration and their traceability back to the national or international source.

Occasionally, there is no standard source for a particular measurement. In these cases, the manufacturer of the measuring equipment or developer of the test will usually provide its own standard. You are required to record the basis of those standards not traceable back to any national or international source. This is simply a record of where the standard came from and why no other standard exists.

Identify calibration status

Users of measuring equipment need to know if the equipment is calibrated and ready for use. This is often accomplished through calibration stickers, but it can also be accomplished through the use of serial numbers, paint dabs, unique markings, and other means that provide traceability to the proof of calibration. The more visual and obvious the indicator, the less likely someone will use equipment that's not in calibration.

Prevent unauthorized adjustments

All measuring equipment must be protected from unauthorized adjustments. For example, if there is an adjustment screw on the back of the gage, access to this screw would need to be restricted. This can be accomplished with labels, wax coatings, or even training that instructs personnel not to make unauthorized adjustments.

Protect from damage

Measuring equipment is often quite delicate and sensitive. That's why ISO 9001:2015 requires that you protect it from damage or deterioration. There are many ways to protect measuring equipment, but here are the most common:

- Use the equipment in the manner in which it was designed and train personnel in the correct use.
- Store equipment in the appropriate location when not in use.
- Maintain the appropriate environment for use of measuring instruments. Because of the sensitivity of many instruments, areas low in dust, grime, temperature extremes, and humidity are usually necessary to ensure accurate results.

Check previous results when out of calibration

When the measuring equipment is found to be out of calibration, we have to evaluate what effect its condition might have had on previous measuring results. This can be achieved by examining how far out of calibration the gage was. If the gage was only slightly out of calibration and well within the product tolerances for the product or process it verifies, we don't have much of a problem. If, on the other hand, the gage was far out of calibration, then we might have to re-measure or recall our products. Whatever your decision is regarding the gage in question, you must record your decision and what action was taken. Any time a piece of measuring equipment is found to be out of calibration, it should trigger an investigation into how product may have been affected.

Records of calibration and verification?

ISO 9001:2015 requires records of fitness for purpose of monitoring and measuring resources, and calibration certainly falls into this category. Make sure your records of calibration include the following:

- Unique identification of the equipment
- Date of calibration
- Who performed calibration
- Results of the calibration and whether the results were within calibration tolerances
- Any necessary adjustments
- Results of the calibration after adjustment
- Unique identification of the standards used in calibration
- Calibration status of the standards used

When equipment is found to be out of calibration, remember to investigate the effect it might have had on product and process and keep a record of this.

A calibration strategy

Everything we've discussed related to calibration is simple enough, but getting started is sometimes difficult. Here's a good strategy for establishing and/or improving a calibration system:

1. *Take a comprehensive inventory of all measuring equipment, gages, instruments, and standards.* Decide what measuring equipment is necessary to ensure valid results.

2. *Create a master gage list for all the measuring equipment that must be calibrated or verified.* The master gage list is your coordination tool and

should be posted prominently and made available to all personnel. A database could be used in place of a list, but databases are often not understandable at a glance. The point of a list is to make the calibration process transparent and clear.

3. *Establish a separate file for each piece of measuring equipment.* These files are where you will maintain records on each gage. This will simplify record keeping and save you from having to dig through a huge jumble of paper when you need a calibration certificate. Don't forget to make a file for gages that are used as standards.

4. *Calibrate all measuring equipment and label each with a calibration sticker (or other indicator).* The sticker should have the date the calibration was performed, who performed it, and when it's next due. In cases where a sticker is impossible, you can get creative by having the sticker in a nearby place and using a serial number to provide traceability to the record.

5. *Generate a calibration record (different from the calibration sticker) for each calibration and make sure that it's maintained in the file for each of the respective gages.* Make sure the calibration record includes all necessary information. Make sure that your control of records procedure addresses calibration records.

7.1.6 Organizational knowledge

No equivalent requirements in ISO 9001:2008. Completely new.

Organizational knowledge is one of the more puzzling new requirements in ISO 9001:2015. Is the standard talking about documentation, training, records, communication, corrective actions, or something else entirely? This subclause strives to create a process for the organization to learn from its successes and failures in a sustainable way. Are there already ways to do this within the standard? Yes, of course. These processes are well established, but they're often overlooked. Let's examine some opportunities for organizational learning:

- A supervisor had been on the job for 20 years. During his tenure, he created a handwritten notebook of procedures addressing particularly difficult aspects of running his department. The notebook had been identified as "uncontrolled documentation" a number of times during internal audits. When the supervisor left the job, the notebook was tossed in the garbage by someone cleaning out his desk.

- One of a company's most valuable customers got into the habit of calling customer service with ideas on how to improve the company's service. The customer service representative politely listened to the suggestions—and even took notes—but she wasn't sure what to do with the suggestions. They didn't constitute problems, so she didn't enter them into the customer complaint database. The suggestions didn't really fit on a customer feedback form, so she didn't record them there either. Ultimately, nothing happened to the suggestions.

- A company introduced an entirely new product line. The roll-out of the products took much longer than expected because of unanticipated problems with suppliers, personnel development, subcontractors, trial production runs, and shipping delays. At the end of the project, the managers involved wrote a long list of "lessons learned" on a white board in the conference room. They wanted to remember the information because another new product line was planned for the next year. A few weeks went by, and finally somebody erased the white board because they needed it to draw a flow diagram.

- A new employee was hired from the local community college. He started as an assistant manager in the warehouse, and came with many years of experience at a similar company. Faced with problems that seemed to only be understood through "tribal knowledge," he created a troubleshooting guide that provided solutions for nearly anything that could go wrong in the department, from paperwork to packaging. The department manager told him to get rid of the troubleshooting guide because "It's not one of our official procedures."

In each of these examples, the information was served to the organization on a silver platter, but the organization failed convert it to knowledge. The failures were many:

- No retained or maintained documented information (i.e., records or documents)
- No analysis of the information
- No communication of the information to key stakeholders

- No transformation of the information into knowledge
- No sustainability of the knowledge

It's worth noting that information doesn't become knowledge until your organization knows its effects, that it's been applied effectively, and that it's sustainable. Figure 5.1 shows the relationship between information and knowledge.

It's common for organizations not to learn from their experiences. The challenge for your organization as you implement ISO 9001:2015 is to build a process that forces learning and makes knowledge collection and dissemination systematic. There are two kind of knowledge that the standard requires you to determine:

- Knowledge for operating your processes
- Knowledge for producing products and services that meet requirements

These are *minimums*, of course. Your organization could collect knowledge on a wide variety of other topics, and it certainly should.

ISO 9001:2015 requires that the knowledge be maintained. This means it will be documented, which could be achieved through a variety of means. The most intuitive way would be a relational database. The database would have different fields representing aspects of the information collected. Being a

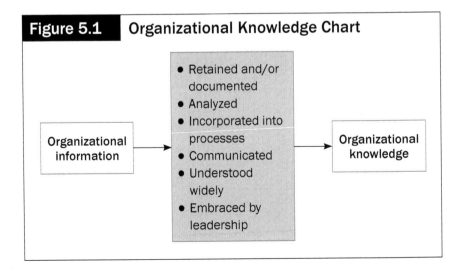

Figure 5.1   Organizational Knowledge Chart

Organizational information →

- Retained and/or documented
- Analyzed
- Incorporated into processes
- Communicated
- Understood widely
- Embraced by leadership

→ Organizational knowledge

database, the fields would be searchable and formattable in a variety of ways. A logical selection of fields might include:

- *Date.* The date that the potential knowledge was received.
- *Entered by.* The person who entered the potential knowledge into the database. The more people you have entering potential wisdom, the better.
- *Source of information.* Where the information came from. This could be a customer, supplier, interested party, or many other sources.
- *Knowledge.* Description of information or knowledge in as much detail as necessary.
- *Reviewed by.* The person(s) responsible for reviewing the potential knowledge so the organization can determine how to use it.
- *Disposition.* A short description of where and how the potential knowledge will be applied.

Besides being maintained, the standard requires that organizational knowledge be made available as necessary. The entire database could be available to employees, or you could share only a subset. The only wrong answer would be to treat the knowledge as a secret and limit its access. Information hasn't been converted to knowledge until people know about it and are able to practically apply it.

As circumstances change, the need for knowledge changes. ISO 9001:2015 requires that the organization examine its current knowledge and decide what additional knowledge is needed and where it will come from. One of the inputs to management review is changes to external and internal issues. When top management reviews these changes, they could also consider existing knowledge and identify any gaps. Clearly, the pursuit of knowledge is continual. The organization just has to establish a disciplined way of capturing and using it.

7.2 COMPETENCE

Equivalent to clause 6.2 of ISO 9001:2008.

It's notable that the word "training" isn't in the title of this clause. Training isn't prohibited, of course, but it's now viewed as simply one of many ways to ensure people have the needed competence. The standard defines competency as a mix of education, training, skills, and experience. Different roles in the organization have different competency requirements, and the trick is to determine what's needed for the employees to perform effectively.

What competencies are needed?

The organization must decide what specific competencies are necessary for someone to perform effectively. Competency requirements can be developed for individual jobs or groupings of similar jobs; it all depends on the organization's needs. I've seen simple organizations that had four sets of competencies that addressed everyone and more complex organizations that had hundreds of different competency standards.

To be fully effective and useful, competency requirements must meet the following requirements. These aren't specific ISO 9001:2015 requirements, but they are practical matters that should at least be considered.

- *Realistic.* Competency requirements must reflect the needs of the activity being performed. Venerable job descriptions, although dog-eared and handed down through the years, may not provide much guidance. Observe the jobs being performed and then talk to the people performing the jobs and to their supervisors. If practical, get input from the customer (internal or external) who receives the job's output. Be careful not to overstate competency needs; make sure that a job really requires a college degree and two years of experience before designating these as competency needs.

- *Demonstrable.* The person performing the activity must be able to demonstrate his or her competencies, particularly as they relate to skills. This means that the organization must be specific and descriptive when defining competency. "Excellent communication skills" is very vague. Take this statement and deconstruct it into its demonstrable elements: Ability to prepare written reports using computer word processing programs; ability to prepare and deliver formal presentations to top management using audio-visual tools. With clearly demonstrable competency needs established, it's much easier to identify gaps.

- *Forward-looking.* The organization should consider its future needs— as far as they can be predicted—as well as present needs. This is where training and strategy begin to intersect. Of course, if strategy hasn't been communicated throughout the organization, this intersection won't be possible. Keep in mind that the forward-looking view of competence must still be based in reality. Competency needs probably can't be projected more than a year into the future and still remain realistic.

- *Maintained as documented information.* ISO 9001 doesn't specifically require that competency needs be documented, but it does say that they must be determined. "Determine" is one of those words that comes very close to document. Without documentation of some sort, how will the organization ensure consistent application and communication of competencies? Document control would most certainly apply to documented competency needs.

Employees whose work affects the QMS

ISO 9001:2015 defines exactly which employees must be addressed in the organization's competence process. At first glance, its focus seems quite narrow: Personnel performing work that affects the QMS. However, if you take a broad view of the organization, you begin to understand that everyone's work affects the QMS at some level. The competence process must include the full range of personnel performing work affecting the QMS, including:

- Top management
- Salaried personnel
- Hourly personnel
- Supervisors and managers
- Temporary employees
- Research and technical personnel
- Recent hires

Many employees can be grouped together based on common roles and job functions; two employees with different job titles won't necessarily have different competency requirements. The converse is also true: Personnel working in the same area and doing ostensibly the same job may actually have differing competency requirements. It's helpful to think about the organization as a series of processes rather than as a collection of departments. The determination of competency requirements is an eye-opening exercise when performed thoughtfully.

Personnel shall be competent

This requirement mandates that everyone who affects the QMS (i.e., everyone in the organization) must be competent. So, what exactly is "competent?" It's the condition that enables a person to perform a task in a manner that meets the required performance standard. ISO 9001:2015 clarifies the issue by establishing that competence is the practical application of four variables:

- *Education.* Education is formal knowledge-building that takes place over an extended time frame, typically delivered through a school of some sort. The traditional method of delivering education is through classroom instruction, although online education has become popular in recent years.

- *Training.* Training is concentrated learning that focuses on a practical application. Most formal educational programs require months or years to complete, but training can often be completed in a matter of hours. The goal of training is usually to equip the student with the ability to perform a very specific task or set of tasks.

- *Skills.* Skills are abilities that personnel are able to apply, and are developed through training or experience. In this way, skills are usually the products of effective training or experience. Some skills are required by personnel before they are even considered for a position, while other skills are developed over time.

- *Experience.* Experience is defined as direct participation in an activity, job, or role. Whereas training and education can be somewhat abstract, experience is concrete. Some jobs require a significant amount of experience because training and education don't provide full exposure to the necessary abilities.

The mix of these four variables—education, training, skills, and experience—will obviously differ depending on the type of job being analyzed. A college professor's competency needs are overwhelmingly concentrated around education and training, with relatively less emphasis on tangible skills and experience. A glass blower, on the other hand, probably requires a great many more skills developed through experience. Just as the college professor and glass blower have drastically different competency needs, most employees' competencies span a wide range, depending on the activities being performed.

Act to obtain competency

Once competency requirements have been determined for all personnel affecting product conformity, the organization must compare individuals to its competency needs and identify where gaps exist. Actions are then taken to close the gaps. A wide range of actions can satisfy gaps in competency. Examples include:

- On-the-job training
- Classroom training
- Independent study (traditional, audio, video, and Internet-based)
- Degree and certificate programs through colleges and universities
- Coaching and counseling
- Opportunities to attend seminars and conferences
- Apprenticeship programs
- Assignment of mentors or role models
- Transferring to other jobs to gain experience or better match existing competency

Obviously, competency building should be applied in as timely a manner possible after gaps have been identified. Allowing a significant amount of time to pass will only diminish the relevance of actions. Keep in mind that training is a complex undertaking and shouldn't be implemented randomly. Just like everything else in the management system, training must be carefully planned. Even on-the-job training must be well planned and carefully provided. In fact, due to the wide range of variables that interact in the job environment, on-the-job training usually requires even more planning. The planning will specify time frames, expectations, and measures.

Evaluate effectiveness

Once actions have been taken, the organization must ensure that its goal—employee competence—has been met. This evaluation can take place in a number of ways, but the most obvious is a demonstration of the newly developed skills or abilities. This works especially well for competency building aimed at skills and training. "OK, we've talked about the task and we've demonstrated how it should be performed. Now you give it a try." If the trainee is able to effectively perform the task while being observed, then he or she could be reasonably considered competent. Keep in mind that the observation period could be an hour, a day, a week, or a month. It all depends on the complexity of the skill being demonstrated. Most on-the-job training programs focus on this kind of evaluation. The trainee starts out as an apprentice and then gradually begins performing many of the tasks independently. The training culminates in the trainee being able to demonstrate the full range of skills involved with the job.

The inspection of an employee's work or product can verify that competence has been achieved. For employees who produce a tangible good or deliver a service, this is often a reasonable indicator of whether training has had the desired effect. Many organizations already have existing systems for inspecting their products. These systems can be channeled into the training program, but this will only work if the product's inspection is traceable back to individual employees.

Tests and examinations can be used to ensure competence, especially when the competence is related to knowledge and facts. Be aware that many individuals simply don't perform well on formal tests or examinations, regardless of the quality of the instruction and training materials, so this may not be an ideal measure of effectiveness. Another drawback is that tests are heavy on administration, requiring someone to spend a great deal of time creating the tests, making sure that all learning objectives are addressed, creating answer keys and a grading scale, grading the tests, dealing with test anxiety and disappointment, and so on. However, tests and examinations have the advantage of resulting in a numerical score that is easy to quantify and track over time.

Finally, some organizations use performance reviews to judge employee competence. Most organizations already use performance reviews of some sort. As long as a logical connection can be made between the training and the job performance, the system will work. One caution, however: Make sure to separate the record of performance review from the record of training effectiveness evaluation, as every organization seeking to keep or gain ISO 9001 registration will be required to provide evidence of the evaluation to its third-party auditor. Showing performance review records to outside parties will create ethical (as well as legal) problems, so you're far better off maintaining separate files.

Keep records of all competency activities

Record keeping is the last major issue to consider within the competency program. ISO 9001:2015 specifically requires you to retain documented information (i.e., records) as evidence of competence. This can be accomplished in a single record or multiple records. The fewer individual records, the better—particularly if the records are kept on paper.

Electronic training records are the most common approach for most organizations. They clearly and quickly show what training has taken place or is planned and make training gaps obvious. Anyone who has been through a QMS audit of paper training records will understand the pitfalls of this approach. The long-term costs of administering electronic records are usually much less than the costs of administering paper records, as well. If you do decide to take this route, make sure to maintain appropriate backup of all electronic files.

7.2 FREQUENTLY ASKED QUESTIONS

The CEO of our company is the owner. We have no ability to make him undergo training, skill building, or anything else. Do we have to establish competency requirements for him?

Yes. Competency requirements must be established for all personnel who affect the performance and effectiveness of the QMS, and the owner and CEO certainly does this

7.2 FREQUENTLY ASKED QUESTIONS

Do training records need to include the signatures of the people who were trained?

There is nothing in ISO 9001:2015 that requires signatures on training records (i.e., retained documented information). However, there may be internal, statutory, or regulatory requirements that require signatures on training records.

All our employees arrive to the organization fully competent, with significant experience, education, training, and skills. There's no additional training we need to provide. Is that OK?

At the very least, personnel typically need to be trained on the relevant aspects of your organization's QMS. No level of incoming competency will provide this type of information.

Do we have to include temporary workers within our competency process? Some of them are only with us a couple of days.

Yes, you must include all personnel who affect the performance and effectiveness of the QMS. Exactly what the competency requirements are is up to you.

7.3 AWARENESS

Equivalent to clause 6.2 of ISO 9001:2008, with some minor additions.

This section of ISO 9001:2015 is a compilation of previous requirements, along with a couple of new requirements thrown in. The title "Awareness" is perfectly apt, as you're simply making employees aware of certain things. They're not expected to be experts on any of the topics. Awareness can be achieved through a meeting, email, newsletter, discussion, bulletin board, training, or whatever other method you deem appropriate. The proof of having done it is the employee's understanding of the topic. Here are the topics you must ensure employees are aware of:

- *The quality policy.* Employees should be aware of the quality policy's existence and what it means to them. Some key words or concepts are all that's necessary. Most quality policies discuss the organization at such an abstract level that it would be hard to say much more than a few key words. Employees could also demonstrate awareness by describing how their own tasks and activities help support the concepts included in the quality policy.

- *Quality objectives.* The organization's quality objectives have a sharper edge than the quality policy. They're more specific and actionable. An awareness of the quality objectives will be harder to achieve simply because the topic is much tighter. An effective awareness campaign on objectives usually includes the following elements:
  - ✓ Description of the objectives and what they indicate
  - ✓ Explanation of why the objective is important to the organization's success
  - ✓ Illustration of how employees can contribute to objectives in their day-to-day activities

During an audit, it's common for personnel to be asked what objectives apply to their jobs and how they contribute to them. Make sure that everybody understands this in clear terms. It's important from the standpoint of an audit, but much more important from the standpoint of effective operations.

- *How employees contribute to the QMS.* The majority of employees contribute to the QMS by correctly applying its various components in their jobs. They access documents, utilize training, contribute to organizational knowledge, and monitor and measure processes and products. Simply make employees aware of the QMS tools and their correct use. The two biggest benefits of improved performance are customer loyalty and the long-term success of the organization. These are obvious, but it's a message that can't be sent too often.

- *What could happen if the QMS is not followed.* This is a fun topic. You're making employees aware of all the bad things that can happen if they don't conform with the QMS (i.e., correctly use the tools of the QMS). Here are a few of the negative effects:
  - ✓ Nonconforming product

✓ Dissatisfied customers
✓ Wasted resources
✓ Higher costs
✓ Loss of sales
✓ Reduction of profit
✓ Greater organization risk
✓ Potential loss of employment

The list goes on and on. Ideally, employees should be able to discuss the implications of not conforming with the QMS in their specific part of the operation. The whole point of this awareness is to drive home the significance of the QMS. It's not an optional program. The QMS is literally how we run the company and stay in business.

7.3 FREQUENTLY ASKED QUESTIONS

Do we have to keep records of making employees aware of the quality policy, quality objectives, and the like? We view the awareness activity as being very similar to training.

No. Strictly speaking, ISO 9001:2015 doesn't require records of awareness activities, though it does require records as evidence of competence. It all depends on how you view this activity and what sort of accountability you need.

7.4 COMMUNICATION

Equivalent to subclause 5.5.3 of ISO 9001:2008, with new planning requirements.

There have been communication requirements in previous versions of ISO 9001, but they were weak compared to this. ISO 9001:2015 requires a fully proactive approach to communications. In essence, the organization is required to develop and implement a communication strategy. This doesn't mean that you can't communicate messages on the spur of the moment as information is needed. Of course, you can. It simply means that the organization must at least have a communication strategy in place and use it as a starting point. ISO 9001:2015 lays out a five-point structure for a communication plan:

1. *What are you trying to communicate?* This is exactly what it sounds like. What message do you want to share? Examples might include monthly production numbers, orders to be shipped, status of regulatory permits, and employee anniversaries with the company. ISO 9001:2015 doesn't require you to maintain documented information of these details, but I've never seen an effective "plan" that wasn't documented in some manner.

2. *When are you going to communicate?* For the various topics identified by the organization, when will the communication take place? Answers might include "the third Thursday of every month" or "9:00 a.m. every Monday." There are no right or wrong answers to frequency and timing of your communications. The plan is simply an attempt to establish some discipline and accountability around the process of communication.

3. *Who are you communicating with?* Every communication must have a target audience. The more targeted, the better. In these days of information overload, it's important to tailor the message to the audience. Define exactly who the audience is for each type of communication and make sure the content of the message is appropriate.

4. *How are you going to communicate?* The choice of communication media is almost limitless. Sometimes the high-tech option is not the best option, however. Consider the sensitivity and importance of the message and the need for two-way dialogue.

5. *Who is the communication coming from?* In other words, who is responsible for making sure the message is heard? The more critical the message, the more likely the communicator will be a member of top management.

Here are some examples of how this sort of planning might look like for some different types of communications:

- Daily production meeting
  1. *What:* Orders in process and orders due to be shipped
  2. *When:* Monday through Friday at 9:00 a.m.

3. *Who to:* Department managers, supervisors, and shift leads
4. *How:* Stand-up meeting beside the time clock, approximately 10 minutes in length
5. *Who from:* Plant manager

- Employee news
  1. *What:* Employee birthdays, work anniversaries, and family announcements
  2. *When:* Monthly, on the third Thursday
  3. *Who to:* All active employees at the Atlanta facility
  4. *How:* Company newsletter emailed to each employee and posted on bulletin boards
  5. *Who from:* Manager of human resources

- Corrective actions and complaints
  1. *What:* Current status of all corrective actions and customer complaints, including new proposals for action
  2. *When:* Friday afternoon at 1:00 p.m.
  3. *Who to:* Improvement team members
  4. *How:* In-person meeting in the North conference room (unless otherwise announced)
  5. *Who from:* Quality assurance technician

- Regulatory overview
  1. *What:* New regulations on the federal state and local level. Also current status of all permits and inspections.
  2. *When:* Quarterly in January, April, July, and October. Exact date and time to be announced.
  3. *Who to:* Environmental health and safety representatives, lab supervisors
  4. *How:* Teleconference (audio and video)
  5. *Who to:* Director of regulatory affairs

It would be impossible to identify all communications generated by the organization. Just cast a big net and try to capture the important ones. Documenting your communication plan in a matrix similar to the one shown in figure 5.2 would make a simple and user-friendly tool that everybody would understand. Is documentation required? No. ISO 9001:2015 makes no mention of retained or maintained documented information, but undocumented plans are very difficult to communication consistently.

Communications at Tech Systems Inc.

Nobody believes in communication more than Darryl Keeler. As president of Tech Systems Inc., communication is possibly the single biggest part of his job. After all, Tech Systems Inc. (*www.techsystemsinc.com*) is a security systems integrator with employees in 32 states, Canada, and Puerto Rico. Being a medium-sized company with business across such a wide geographic area has its challenges. Keeler long ago decided that robust and continuous communication needed to be a guiding principle.

"Communication is the key factor in maintaining a high level of employee satisfaction," says Keeler. "And satisfied well-informed employees ensure that we have highly satisfied clients."

Keeler writes the "Friday Finale," a weekly newsletter that goes out to every employee. It maintains a warm touch, covering birthdays, work anniversaries, and anything of importance that's happening with teammates. It also addresses business updates from the previous week.

"TSI Family Emails" (TSI stands for Tech Systems Inc.) is the company's way of communicating items that are of high importance to the entire company, sort of "red alert" emails. These include process changes, policy changes, and major customer developments. The "TSI Family Emails" are one step beyond the "Friday Finales" in terms of business importance.

The "Tour De Focus" is one of the company's most impressive communication media. This is where Keeler travels around the country and meets with every employee. He sits down and asks for comments or opportunities for the company to improve based on individual opinions. These are all captured and recorded, and the leadership team works through all of them and gets back with the people who suggested the improvements. This entire list is posted on SharePoint for everyone to review, and the ideas always number in the hundreds. The employee portal is the live repository of information that team members use

Figure 5.2   Communication Plan Example

WHAT	WHEN	WHO TO	HOW	WHO FROM
Daily production meeting	Monday through Friday at 9 a.m.	Department managers, supervisors, and shift leads	Stand-up meeting beside the time clock, approximately 10 minutes in length	Plant manager
Employee news	Monthly, on the third Thursday	All active employees at the Atlanta facility	Company newsletter emailed to each employee and posted on bulletin boards	Manager of human resources
Corrective actions and complaints	Friday afternoon at 1 p.m.	Improvement team members	In-person meeting in the North conference room (unless otherwise announced)	Quality assurance technician
Regulatory overview	Quarterly in January, April, July, and October. Exact date and time TBD.	EH&S representatives, lab supervisors	Teleconference (audio and video)	Director of regulatory affairs
Audit results	Within two days of each internal audit	All employees	Posted on the company intranet page (quality tab)	Quality manager
Media publications about company	Within one day of original publication	All employees	Posted on the company intranet page (media tab)	Manager of human resources
Status of quality objectives	Updated monthly	All employees	Posted on the company intranet page (home page)	Quality manager

for their jobs. Only the most current versions of documents are available, and it also includes phone lists, updates, tutorials, and training materials.

Finally, the leadership team of Tech Systems meets every Monday to go over financials, hot company topics, and opportunities for improvement. The Monday meeting also serves as the primary feeder of information into the company's monthly management review. Communication is the oil that flows through the engine of Tech Systems Inc. And the president of the company is head mechanic and communicator.

7.4 FREQUENTLY ASKED QUESTIONS

We wrote a communication program, but we've already violated it a couple of times by not performing the communication specified. Is this a potential audit finding?

Yes. If you've made a commitment to perform certain communication activities, then it's a requirement of the QMS. This is especially the case if the commitment is documented.

7.5 DOCUMENTED INFORMATION

Equivalent to subclauses 4.2.3 and 4.2.4 of ISO 9001:2008.

The distinction between documents and records is gone in ISO 9001:2015. All we have now is "documented information." Why did they take such a clear-cut concept and mess around with it? After all, most quality practitioners have a pretty clear understanding of the differences. Just to make sure we're all on the same page, let's do a quick review:

- *Document.* Living information that is used for decision making or performing tasks. Subject to revision. Think of such things as procedures, policies, instructions, and blank checklists. We usually think about "following" documents because they tend to guide us.
- *Records.* Historical information about things that have already happened. What did we do last week, last month, last year? Not subject to change because you can't change what already happened.

Previous versions of ISO 9001 had separate sections of requirements for documents and records. They are different from a theoretical standpoint, but things have begun to merge somewhat with the widespread use of digital information. Both documents and records are likely to be digital files that employees access in much the same way. So the writers of ISO 9001:2015 decided to address them together.

Despite the universal use of the term "documented information," there are clues to let you know whether the standard is asking for a document or a record. If ISO 9001:2015 requires you to "retain documented information," it means a record. If ISO 9001:2015 requires you to "maintain documented information," it means a document. Everything hinges on the terms "retain" vs. "maintain." There are plenty of places in the standard that neither require you to retain nor maintain documented information. ISO 9001:2015 seems to require nothing other than an understanding among the people working within the process. Keep in mind that another way of describing this situation is "tribal knowledge," which doesn't make for a very effective QMS. Use your own good sense when deciding what to document or record. Just because ISO 9001:2015 doesn't explicitly require you to retain or maintain documented information doesn't mean you shouldn't do it.

You're also not required to use the clunky phrases "retain documented information" and "maintain documented information." If your organization uses the terms records and documents—and everybody understands what these words mean—then you certainly don't have to change your language. Always strive for simplicity and clarity in your QMS. Few people would argue that the new terms used by ISO 9001:2015 are simpler and clearer. Along those same lines, if you presently have a separate document control procedure and a control of records procedure, you're under no obligation to combine them. Do what makes sense to you and your organization.

Before we go any further, it's important to say this: If you already have document control and records control procedures that meet ISO 9001:2008's requirements, then you already meet ISO 9001:2015's requirements.

ISO 9001:2015 begins this section by saying that your QMS should include documented information required by the standard and documented information needed by your organization. These requirements are obvious and clear, and probably didn't even need to be stated. More helpful are the notes at the end of clause 7.5. They basically say that the type and quantity of documented information (documents and records) will differ from company to company, because everybody is different. Don't blindly adopt documented information just because somebody recommends it. Examine the benefit and make an informed decision. The more voluminous your documentation becomes, the less likely employees are to use or understand it.

Your system for managing documented information doesn't itself have to be documented. That's a big change from ISO 9001:2008, which required documented procedures for both document control and control of records. Now you just have to make sure you ensure the following practices are in place when you create and update documented information:

- *Identification.* Documents and records must have titles, document numbers, or something that indicates their identity. As long as you can differentiate between different documented information, knowing which ones address which topics, then you've met this requirement.

- *Format.* The documents must be usable for their purpose. The format must be appropriate to the purpose and users, and the media must be accessible and understandable. For example, if the medium is electronic, then users would need to have access to a computer or other interface that can display the electronic media. Another example might relate to a company that has a high percentage of employees who don't speak English; their documentation would need to be graphically formatted (to make language irrelevant) or translated into the language predominantly spoken by the employees.

- *Review and approval.* Somebody must review and approve the documented information before it's used. Who performs this function is completely up to you. There are many different ways to signify review and approval: signatures, initials, email approval, electronic signatures, meeting minutes, or click-box approval within a document control program. Review and approval does have to be traceable, meaning it must be clear who performed it. It should also be secure, which means the organization has prevented imposters from making reviews/approvals under somebody else's name.

Once the documented information exists, the next logical step is control. Here are the control requirements from ISO 9001:2015:

- *Availability.* The documented information exists where it's supposed to exist. The organization has dedicated the resources to create the documented information and the information is suitable for the need it was intended to fill.

- *Protection.* The documented information is protected from tampering, unauthorized changes, and damage. People who shouldn't see the documented information are prevented from seeing it. Appropriate safeguards put in place by the organization to ensure information isn't misused in any way. System passwords and employee training are two ways to accomplish this.

- *Distribution.* You can access the documented information. Employees don't struggle to find it, and they understand how to interpret its meaning. If a computer or program is necessary to access the documented information intended for employees, then employees can operate it. In the case of retained information (e.g., records), they can be retrieved within a reasonable amount of time.

- *Storage.* The organization specifies where the documented information is located. This applies to retained documented information (records) and maintained documented information (documents). The location is accurate and verifiable, and there are controls to preserve the information. Preservation could include periodic backups of computer files and periodic monitoring to ensure continued legibility. The controls for "preservation" are very similar to the controls for "protection," described above.

- *Change control.* The organization is able to ensure that the correct versions of documented information are available. When documented information is revised, the revisions are incorporated into the information in use (after review and approval). There are safeguards in place to prevent employees from incorrectly accessing and using obsolete information.

- *Retention.* We say how long we retain documented information. Remember, the term "retain" refers to records, so this is the requirement for establishing a retention time. Every record in your system could conceivably have a different retention time, and ISO 9001:2015 provides no guidance on the appropriate retention times of records. This is completely up to the organization and its needs. Disposition refers to what happens to the record after the retention times has elapsed. Typical dispositions include archive, shred, or recycle.

Finally, ISO 9001:2015 addresses external documents and preventing unintended alterations of retained information.

An external document is published outside the organization and used within the scope of the management system. Examples of external documents possibly requiring control include:

- Troubleshooting and/or calibration manuals published by equipment manufacturers
- Test procedures, specifications, and/or engineering drawings published by customers or other bodies
- Instructions, specifications, and/or procedures published by suppliers
- Standards published by industrial organizations applicable to the organization
- International standards such as ISO 9001

Once external documents have been determined, they must be identified, and they must be controlled. Like internal documents, there must be a title, document number, or other unique identifier. Such identification typically comes from the source that publishes the document, and the organization simply adopts it. Make sure that all the other aspects of "control" are applied to external documents.

The last requirement provided by ISO 9001:2015 concerns retained documented information that provides evidence of conformity. In other words, records that prove you met requirements. I would say that this statement applies to all records. The organization must ensure that people can't make unauthorized changes to records. This is a restatement of the protection and preservation requirements already discussed.

What to control?

"Do I need to control this?" is one of the most frequently asked questions in organizations working toward, or maintaining, a formal management system. Given the universe of documented information possibly requiring control, the question is understandable. Besides, most people would rather not control something if they don't have to. Here are some questions to ask when determining whether a document should be controlled:

- Does the documented information guide the production of products (i.e., goods or services) provided by the organization?
- Does the documented information guide the verification, inspection, or testing of products provided by the organization?
- Does the documented information define customer and/or product requirements?
- Is the documented information used for controlling processes?
- Is the documented information used for decision making by production personnel?
- Is the documented information used for collecting data that could be used later for decision making within the scope of the management system (e.g., a form)?
- Is the information so critical that failure to keep it updated would pose a risk to the organization or its customers?
- Does the documented information address or relate to a requirement from ISO 9001?

If the answer to one or more of these questions is yes, then the documented information should probably be controlled. For illustration purposes, consider the following scenarios:

- *An interoffice memo is posted on a wall in the fabrication department.* The memo gives a number of functional and packaging requirements for a product that's fabricated there. Because of where the document has been posted and the information it contains, the memo should be controlled. Ignore the fact that memos are rarely controlled; in this case it provides customer requirements, guides decision making, and relates directly to ISO 9001 requirements. Even if the memo duplicates information contained elsewhere in controlled specifications, the uncontrolled memo would still be a problem. Eventually, there will be a discrepancy between the information on the memo and the information contained in the controlled specifications. The organization should either control the posted memo or get rid of it.

- *A training department develops videos to train employees on the proper setup and operation of production lines.* The videos are included in the training program for new hires and existing employees. In this case, document control is required because the videos define process control, guide the production of products, and relate to the training requirements of ISO 9001.
- *Product defect samples are displayed in a lighted glass cabinet in the visual inspection area.* The samples illustrate the limits of various defects that can be considered acceptable to customers, and they're used when inspectors aren't certain of the criteria. Currently, the display cabinet is labeled "for reference only." Despite this declaration, the samples should be controlled because they define customer requirements.
- *An organization develops a checklist that's used to record the results of product inspection.* The blank checklist defines exactly what's to be inspected as indicated by the spaces that inspectors must complete. These blank forms need to be controlled as documents and then as records once they're completed.

These scenarios highlight the fact that documented information needn't be limited to traditional procedures, work instructions, and the like. The term "documented information" can encompass a wide range of things, all of which might require control, depending on the information they contain. Some examples include:

- Databases
- Photos
- Drawings, diagrams, and sketches
- Audio and video
- Product samples and defect samples
- Paint swatches for color matching
- Checklists
- Flow diagrams
- Blank forms

ISO 9001:2015 doesn't require you to write a procedure for how you control documented information. Should you do it anyway? Yes! It's a potentially complicated topic that should be communicated in a consistent manner. Describe your system within maintained documented information (i.e., a documented procedure) and you'll have much less confusion.

7.5 FREQUENTLY ASKED QUESTIONS

Where is the requirement in ISO 9001:2015 that says we have to follow our own procedures?

There is no specific requirement in ISO 9001:2015 that states this. The expectation is that if you write a procedure within the scope of the management system, then you've committed to implementing it.

Even though ISO 9001:2015 doesn't really distinguish between documents and records, we do. Is it OK if we maintain separate procedures for controlling documents and records?

Yes, of course. I expect that many companies will do this.

Do we need top management to review and approve all our documents?

I certainly hope not. There's nothing in ISO 9001:2015 that would require top management to approve all documents. You decide who must approve documents.

We have a lot of job aids and work instructions in our work areas that are impractical to control. People use the information only occasionally. Can we just stamp all of this "For Reference Only"?

No. Either control the job aids and instructions or get rid of them. Stamping something "For Reference Only" does little to prevent personnel from using the documents to guide their actions and make decisions.

Can we specify two weeks as the retention time for a particular record?

If two weeks is as long as you need to retain a record, then that's your decision. ISO 9001:2015 doesn't provide any guidance on retention times.

Chapter 6

ISO 9001:2015 Section 8 Operation

8.1 OPERATIONAL PLANNING AND CONTROL

Equivalent to clause 7.1 in ISO 9001:2008.

Operational planning and control is all about how you establish, resource, and manage your production processes. You're probably thinking, "My organization has been around for many years, and we've already developed our operation. Do we have to go back and do it again?" No, of course, you don't. You may have to formalize some of your processes, though. You know those checklists that sometimes get completed and sometimes not? They'll need to be consistently completed. You know those inspections that people do when they have time? They need to be done on time, every time. ISO 9001:2015 doesn't require these controls; they're specified by your organization. You plan your product realization so it enables you to consistently create products that meet requirements. No matter what your product is, some kind of planning is required.

Operational planning and control is not a one-shot deal. Your organization must periodically re-examine the operation as circumstances change. Management review is a good place to do this, especially under the input "Changes in external and internal issues that are relevant to the quality management system." When your external and internal issues change, there's a good chance that your existing operation could be affected. Other logical triggers to reconsider your operation are clause 6.3, Planning of changes, and subclause 8.5.6, Control of changes.

If you already did an effective job of addressing the requirements of clause 4.4, Quality management system and its processes, then you've already met the requirements of clause 8.1. Clauses 4.4 and 8.1 are very similar; however, clause 8.1 is less detailed and is specifically focused on the processes for products and services. That doesn't mean that you can't address both simultaneously. You should, and this will help keep your quality management system (QMS) streamlined and concise.

Each of the operational planning and control requirements are explained below. Keep in mind that the requirements are intended to help you focus on the processes you use to create your products and services.

Requirements for products and services

This is one of the most fundamental controls imaginable. What requirements must your products and services satisfy? These requirements can cover almost anything. They might relate to timeliness, size, shape, color, performance, functionality, or anything that a customer or interested party might care about. They generally originate from one of two sources:

- *8.2.2, Determining the requirements related to products and services.* These are the requirements explicitly or implicitly cited by your customers when they ask you to do something. They also include any legal requirements.
- *8.3, Design and development of products and services.* These are the requirements established by your own design process when you create a product or service.

Should these requirements be maintained in documented information (i.e., specification or standard)? Of course. How else are you going to consistently communicate and satisfy them? ISO 9001:2015 gives you the option of documenting or not documenting the requirements, though in most cases documented information of some sort will be needed. Requirements for products and services are typically documented in a specification, standard, or work order, as opposed to a procedure.

Criteria for processes

Your processes are chains of activities and tasks that are linked together with a common purpose. You identified these processes in clause 4.4, Quality management system and its processes. Your organization must determine the criteria for making sure the processes are performing correctly. Criteria might relate to output, speed, efficiency, conformity, pressure, temperature, or any number of other variables. It's dependent on the needs of the process. This is a repeat of an earlier requirement from subclause 4.4(c), which also asked you to determine the criteria for operating your processes.

Acceptance of products and services

All products and services get checked in some way. This is what the standard refers to as "acceptance." The check can be simple or complex, proactive or reactive, but you do something to make sure your product meets requirements. It's up to you to decide what's necessary and when. People find it helpful to think about product and service acceptance in different stages for planning purposes:

- *Incoming.* This is the verification of purchased product or outsourced process. It can be very simple or quite complex, depending on the nature of the incoming product. Purchased product can be a good or a service, and the type of verification is likely to be different for each.
- *In-process.* Before the good or service is completed, it often makes sense to perform a verification. This can prevent later problems and allow for midstream correction.
- *Final.* When the good or service is complete, a final inspection often adds value. In the case of goods, this usually takes place before shipping. In the case of services, it happens at the point of service delivery, often through customer perception.

Decide what makes sense for your given circumstances and plan the activity. We'll address this topic in more detail in clause 8.6, Release of products and services.

Resources needed for conformity

What resources does your operation need to function properly? You determined high-level resources for the entire QMS back in subclause 7.1.1, Resources—general. Now we're talking about specific resources related to how you create your products and services. These might include equipment, machines, utilities, people, raw materials, supplies, or a variety of other resources. Review how you addressed clause 4.4, Quality management system and its processes. If you stated specific resources for operations that create products and services, then you're all done here.

Control of processes against criteria

You've already established the criteria for your processes. Now you're checking to make sure the processes meet your requirements. These can include supervisor oversight, inspections of process output, automated monitoring, comparison against objectives, or other issues. Again, you've probably already addressed this requirement by satisfying clause 4.4.

Documented information

ISO 9001:2015 states that you will determine, maintain, and retain documented information to ensure your processes perform correctly and your products or services meet all requirements. "Determine" is clear enough: Decide what documented information is needed. "Maintain and retain," of course, refer to two different concepts. Maintain refers to documents and retain refers to records. Here are examples of each as they relate to operational planning and control:

- Retain:
  - ✓ Product inspection data
  - ✓ Final inspection reports
  - ✓ Results of visual inspection

✓ First-article inspections
✓ Incoming inspection records
✓ Lab checks
✓ Start-up checklists
✓ Process monitoring data
✓ Process validations

- Maintain:
  ✓ Product specifications
  ✓ Product data sheets
  ✓ Process standards
  ✓ Standard operating procedures
  ✓ Work instructions
  ✓ Product procedures
  ✓ Flowcharts
  ✓ Blank forms
  ✓ Blank checklists

You don't have to adopt all of these examples. You don't necessarily have to adopt any of them. But if you're using these tools—and they ensure your processes perform correctly and your products and services meet all requirements—then they must be appropriately retained and maintained.

Output of planning in a suitable form

The output of all this planning is the management system itself. Your policies, procedures, and records are tangible results of planning. You don't have to produce a document titled "Plan for Product Realization" or "Quality Plan." Just plan your production process, then think about the requirements, processes, resources, and controls that will be needed to achieve conforming products and services.

If an auditor asks to see your operational planning, show him or her your management system documents related to production. Planning is how you knew what you needed. It's that simple.

Planned and unintended changes

Clause 8.1 includes a placeholder that basically says, "Remember to manage change." There are already detailed clauses within ISO 9001:2015 for planned changes (clause 6.3) and unplanned changes (subclause 8.5.6). Just make sure you have processes to address those sections.

Control of outsourcing

Outsourcing is a process that directly affects your product and services, but which is performed by a different organization. Many companies find it cheaper, easier, or more effective to have certain processes performed by someone else. This is especially the case when the process is highly specialized or difficult. Examples include painting, powder coating, plating, anodizing, drilling, polishing, and many others. ISO 9001:2015 simply says that outsourcing must be "controlled." Control could be realized through a wide range of activities, including:

- Clearly indicating requirements on a purchase order
- Carefully qualifying outsourcing partners
- Inspecting outsourced work
- Auditing the outsourcing organization
- Requiring detailed inspection data and reports
- Ensuring that the organization which performs outsourcing is ISO 9001 certified
- Establishing measurable goals for the outsourcing partner
- Meeting on a regular basis to discuss performance
- Providing report cards or scores to the outsourcing partner

Most organizations manage any outsourcing activities as part of their purchasing process. This is discussed in clause 8.4.

8.2 REQUIREMENTS FOR PRODUCTS AND SERVICES

8.2.1 Customer communication

Equivalent to subclause 7.2.3 in ISO 9001:2008.

Customer communication should come naturally, but it rarely does. Organizations must develop explicit processes for customer communication to ensure that it takes place effectively. ISO 9001:2015 requires explicit channels of customer communication: product information, inquiries and changes, feedback, customer property, and contingency requirements. Let's briefly discuss each one.

Product information

If you weren't already communicating about your products, you wouldn't have any customers. It's the most natural kind of communication imaginable. ISO 9001:2015 simply requires that you determine and implement an effective process for communicating about product requirements. Here are some of the most common ways of communicating about products:

- Service agreements
- Product data sheets
- Marketing literature and brochures
- Websites
- Price lists
- Product samples

The most common problem with product information is that it isn't maintained. Make sure that you have an effective process for communicating product information and keeping it up to date. Incorrect product information is a frequent cause of customer complaints, so it clearly has an effect on your success.

Inquiries, orders, and changes

After you provide product information, the next step is (hopefully) an order or a contract. This clause asks you to determine the communication that will effectively manage the transaction. Here are a few words about each type of transactional communication:

- *Inquiries.* How do customers inquire about the availability of product or other information? Sure, you've already provided product information, but it's common for people to have additional questions. Salespeople or customer service personnel often receive inquiries, but they can also be handled by an automated system. Typical ways of handling inquiries include telephone, email, website, database query, or in person. The process for making an inquiry is usually defined within product information.

- *Order handling or contracts.* How does someone place an order or initiate a contract? If there is one kind of communication you want to make simple and intuitive, it's this one. After all, someone is trying to give you money. How difficult do you want to make it? Often the method for placing an order is the same as the method for placing an inquiry, but not always. Clearly specify the method for initiating business and keep the information up to date.

- *Changes.* This is one type of communication that organizations often forget to establish. It acknowledges that customers sometimes change their mind and make mistakes. Most organizations establish time limits for amendments, beyond which a customer is obligated for at least a portion of the cost of the order or contract. You need to let customers know how to amend their orders and clearly communicate the rules and penalties (as applicable).

Customer feedback, including complaints

How does your organization receive customer feedback and complaints? Let your customers know the methods and make it as easy as possible. This is especially important with complaints. Try to avoid complicated processes that discourage dialogue and frustrate customers. A common question is whether this clause requires a formal complaint process. I believe it does. Establish a process for receiving complaints, recording the details, and investigating the causes. Customer complaints don't necessarily have to become corrective actions, but they should at least be investigated and considered for corrective actions.

Smart organizations remind their customers on a regular basis of how to provide feedback and post complaints. The topic of customer feedback is addressed in much more detail in subclause 9.1.2.

Controlling customer property

Not every organization handles or uses customer property, but it's a touchy subject when you do. Customer property includes a wide range of items you use or process in some capacity, but which belong to your customer. What might fall into this category? Here are some of the most common:

- Raw materials
- Specialized equipment
- Measuring devices
- Products returned for repair or warranty work
- Molds and tooling
- Templates and patterns
- Jigs and fixtures
- Returnable containers
- Packaging and labeling
- Intellectual property

This topic is covered in much more detail in subclause 8.5.3, Property belonging to customers or external providers.

Establishing contingency actions

Contingency actions are "what if" scenarios. They certainly don't apply to every transaction an organization initiates. In fact, they may rarely come up, but it's important to consider if any contingency actions might be necessary. Contingency actions are one more way of addressing risk. These might include what will happen in the event of:

- A lost or late shipment
- Product failure in the field
- Delivery during nonbusiness hours
- Weather emergencies
- Labor stoppage (in a unionized environment)

Contingencies are usually defined as part of large, expensive, and risky projects. Evaluate your own contracts and orders to see if this is something your organization would benefit from.

8.2.1 FREQUENTLY ASKED QUESTIONS

We have effective means of communicating with our customers, including a toll-free phone number, website, and frequent meetings. Do we need to document these processes in a procedure?

No, not unless you think it adds value.

8.2.2 Determining the requirements for products and services

Equivalent to subclause 7.2.1 of ISO 9001:2008.

This is where you take orders, write contracts, and determine product requirements. These tasks typically take place in customer service, sales, contracting, or somewhere else where personnel interact directly with customers. However, the process of defining product requirements can take place anywhere. Here are just a few of the many ways that you could determine product requirements:

- Taking orders via telephone, email, or fax
- Meeting with customers in person
- Receiving automated orders via the Internet
- Negotiating contracts
- Receiving a production schedule
- Agreeing to a project plan

The customer who you're determining requirements with may be internal or external to your organization. Product requirements are often determined through a production schedule, project plan, work order, or similar tool for organizations that serve a different part of the same company.

ISO 9001:2015 states that your organization will define product requirements (in all their various facets) and that your organization will be able to meet the claims for its products. Let's explore the product requirements you need to determine.

Requirements are defined

The most logical place to start is with the requirements the customer has explicitly asked for. The customer may request a range of technical and performance requirements or simply reference your own product or service description. Either way, these are the requirements that your customers have in the forefront of their expectations. Here are the type of requirements we're talking about:

- Product or service description
- Performance requirements
- Price
- Quantity
- Timing
- Location of product or service delivery
- Post-delivery activities

These requirements can be captured via telephone, fax, email, website, electronic data interchange (EDI), or in person. The exact mode doesn't really matter as much as its ability to capture exactly what the customer wants. Having a form of some sort that probes the relevant issues (e.g., product description, performance requirements, etc.) will help ensure that all relevant attributes have been addressed. It's a good idea to have no assumptions about what the customer wants.

Statutory and regulatory requirements

Technically, there is a difference between statutory and regulatory requirements. It's a fine difference, though. We'll cover it briefly for the sake of completeness. Statutes are *laws*. They say what you can and can't do in broad terms. Regulations are usually specific guidelines published and enforced by regulatory bodies. The bottom line is that statutes and regulations are both enforced by authorities that can make your life difficult. Understand what statutes and regulations apply to your products, and make sure you're able to meet them. Satisfaction of this clause is typically achieved in a two-part manner:

1. Developing a process for understanding and staying up-to-date with statutes and regulations
2. Compiling an index or listing of statutes and regulations applicable to your products

These processes aren't specifically required by ISO 9001:2015, but they would represent an effective way of meeting subclause 8.2.2's requirements.

It's worth noting that statutes and regulations can come not only from the country in which you are based, but they can also originate from countries in which you're selling your products. Multinational organizations have to consider statutory and regulatory requirements everywhere they operate in the world. Understanding and staying current with statutes and regulations can become somebody's full-time job for companies that operate around the globe.

Subclause 8.2.2 is also very significant for companies that produce highly regulated products. Examples include:

*   Drugs and pharmaceuticals
*   Medical devices
*   Food
*   Aircraft and aircraft parts
*   Explosives and firearms

Address the requirement for statutory and regulatory requirements in the simplest way possible, but keep in mind that for certain organizations this will be a very strategic process.

Requirements not stated by the customer but necessary

These are the requirements your customers don't bother to tell you. Customers assume that certain things will be done, and then don't even think about other requirements. It's the organization's job to fill in the blanks and define the requirements not stated by the customer. These are often addressed through internal specifications or standards for your products. Unless the customer requests otherwise, the internal specification will supplement their requirements. Here are some examples of requirements not stated by the customer, but necessary for specified or intended use:

- *Cleanliness.* Service providers often have internal guidelines for providing a clean product. This is the case for most hotels. Hotel customers rarely ask that their bathroom be cleaned and the carpet vacuumed. This is simply expected, and anything else isn't acceptable to the customer.

- *Packaging.* Customers rarely specify a particular type of packaging for products; they simply expect the product to arrive undamaged. The organization must determine the specific type of packaging that will adequately protect the product. This becomes an internal specification for the organization.

- *Professionalism.* Personnel acting on behalf of your organization are expected to behave professionally. They might be expected to dress in clean clothes, bathe regularly, and speak properly when interacting with customers. A customer would rarely think to specify, "Please don't send any consultants to us who smell bad or swear a lot." It's simply expected that the organization has standards regarding professionalism. Failure to have these standards could certainly affect the conformity of the organization's product.

Think about the requirements your customer needs related to the product but hasn't thought to specify.

Requirements considered necessary by the organization

Not all product requirements come from customers or the law. Some come from the organization itself, because it has deemed them appropriate. Some of these requirements fall into the categories of aesthetics and branding. Here are some examples:

- *Use of logos.* Many organizations require that their logo be affixed to the product and product packaging. There's no functional reason for doing this; it's simply a requirement that the organization determined to reinforce its branding.

- *Uniforms.* Personnel at service companies often wear uniforms. There is rarely any functional reason for this. It's simply a matter of branding and appearance.
- *Collection of feedback.* Some service organizations require that customer feedback be collected at the point of service. This certainly isn't essential to the product itself, but the organization has determined it to be necessary. Because the feedback is collected at the point of service, this is essentially another product requirement.
- *Distribution of marketing materials.* Many organizations include marketing materials when a good or service is delivered. This typically isn't required or requested by the customers, but the organization has made it an internal requirement.

Other requirements determined necessary by the organization may relate to essential functions of the product or service. In other words, the customer didn't ask for it, but the requirement is still necessary. These are often captured in internal specifications that the customer may or may not have had access to. Regardless, it's the organization's responsibility to know about all applicable requirements. Here are some examples:

- A catering company has an internal requirement that its cooked buffet foods be maintained at a temperature of at least 140° F. For the purpose of food safety, the food server monitors the temperature the entire time the food is available. The customer doesn't request this, but it's an essential requirement that the organization must fulfill.
- A shipping company has an internal requirement that all boxes weighing more than 150 pounds must be banded to a wooden pallet before shipping. Again, the customer rarely requests this, but the company knows that if the box is not palletized it will be very difficult to move.
- A hotel maintains a housekeeping checklist that includes such things as cleaning the bathroom fixtures, emptying all wastebaskets, changing bedsheets, and vacuuming the floor. Housekeepers carry out these tasks because they are needed to maintain a hygienic and attractive facility, not because any customers have specifically requested them.

How do all these requirements get documented? We've just discussed product requirements from a number of different angles. ISO 9001:2015 simply requires that you determine these product requirements, but it doesn't provide any guidance on where these go once they've been determined. This is because each organization is likely to have its own way of capturing and communicating product requirements. In a perfect world, all product requirements would be shown clearly in one place. Despite this constant striving for simplicity, this is rarely the way things work. Product requirements are likely to be in more than one place, but as long as you can demonstrate that the requirements are accessible and complete, you have fulfilled the spirit of this clause.

The final sentence of this section asks you to make sure that you meet any claims you make about your product or service. In other words, you can walk the talk. It's unlikely that organizations seeking ISO 9001:2015 certification would make bogus claims about their products, but you never know. The more likely scenario is accidentally making product claims that can't be substantiated. The very next subclause of the standard will help you stay on the straight and narrow with regard to product claims.

8.2.2 FREQUENTLY ASKED QUESTIONS

Do we have to put all the product requirements in the same place? They won't all fit on our sales order.

You don't have to record all the product requirements in the same place. As long you know what they are and can access them, then there's proof that they were determined.

8.2.3 Review of requirements for products and services

Equivalent to subclause 7.2.2 of ISO 9001:2008

8.2.3.1 (No subclause title)

Once you determine product requirements, you must review them. This is really nothing more than a sanity check: Do we understand the requirements and can we really meet them? Most people have had experiences with organizations that promised to do something but badly missed the mark. The intent of this element is to keep you from being one of those organizations.

ISO 9001:2015 requires that you review the order or contract prior to committing to supply it. In practical terms, this is usually the acceptance of the order or contract into your own production system. The customer may have already placed the order, but you haven't formally committed to supply it. This review can be performed by anyone, even the person who took the order in the first place. The review could even be performed by a computer. Specifically, the review includes the following items:

- *Customer requirements.* We discussed determining these requirements in the previous section. Now we're making sure we got the story straight. This is the single most important category of requirements because it comes directly from the customer. Some typical checks that organizations make when performing this review include:
  - ✓ Delivery date requested by the customer
  - ✓ Quantity requested by the customer
  - ✓ Product name or part number referenced by the customer
  - ✓ Price requested by the customer
  - ✓ Any tolerances and specifications requested by the customer
  - ✓ Paperwork, certifications, or reports requested by the customer
  - ✓ Follow-up actions after delivery requested by the customer

This check can be done by a person or by a computer, but either way we're answering two questions:
- ✓ Did we correctly record the customer requirements?
- ✓ Do we have the ability to meet the customer requirements?

If we can answer yes to both of these questions, we can move onto the next item to review.

- *Requirements not stated by the customer but necessary.* Customers rarely ask for everything they need. They make assumptions about the product or service, and they're also ignorant about certain aspects of the product or service. In both cases, it's your organization's job to fill in the blanks. Many of these requirements come from internal specifications or standards that are applied automatically unless the customer requests otherwise. Just make sure you have standards in place to cover product requirements not addressed by customers.

- *Requirements specified by the organization.* These can be anything else you've decided your product or service must meet. They don't come from the customer, and they're not strictly needed to fulfill the product or service. Here are some examples of extra requirements you might apply to your products or services:
  - ✓ Product tests done strictly to satisfy internal requirements
  - ✓ Arrival of service personnel before appointment time to set up
  - ✓ How customers are to be addressed (for instance, "Sir" or "Ma'am")
  - ✓ Training of the customer (which is not requested by the customer or absolutely necessary)
  - ✓ The correct dress and appearance of employees
  - ✓ Use of marketing materials
  - ✓ Placement of logo on product and use of corporate colors
  - ✓ Method of cleanup
  - ✓ Use of recycled or biodegradable materials
  - ✓ Use of "fair trade" raw materials
  - ✓ Upholding of ethical standards
  - ✓ Asking the customer to sign certain paperwork

- *Statutory and regulatory requirements.* As we stated earlier, this is what the law requires of your products and services. Depending on the type of product or service you provide, each contract might get an exhaustive legal review, or you might face a much simpler situation. If you have a highly regulated product, this was likely identified during your planning for risks in clause 6.1. Simply apply the appropriate amount of scrutiny to your orders and contracts in accordance with their statutory and regulatory exposure.

- *Conflicting requirements.* It's not uncommon for an order or contract to involve many exchanges of information, some of which conflict with one another. This is especially true in this age of multiple communication channels. The more communication that takes place—especially among different modes and with different parties—the greater the chance that details will become confused. Just compare all the different communications that may have taken place and make sure that there aren't any conflicts. Here are some examples of how requirements can differ from those previously expressed:

  ✓ Specifications that accompany the order don't match the specifications on file.

  ✓ The customer placed an order via telephone and purchase order, but the purchase order requirements differ from the telephone order requirements.

  ✓ Two different customer representatives are asking for contradictory requirements.

  ✓ The customer becomes confused and requests different delivery dates.

  ✓ The customer asks you to do something that isn't in the contract.

  If you encounter instances when requirements differ, contact the customer and resolve the conflict. Of course, keep a record of contacting the customer and what the final agreement was.

- *Undocumented requirements.* If the customer doesn't provide a documented statement of requirements, as is the case with telephone orders, you must confirm the order back to the customer. This can be as simple as repeating the requirements back to the customer to make sure you understood what he or she wanted. Many organizations email the order to customers so they can review it themselves.

8.2.3 FREQUENTLY ASKED QUESTIONS

We don't take orders or write contracts with customers. All we do is work against a schedule our home office sends us once a week. Can we exclude the requirement of reviewing product requirements?

No. The schedule represents your product requirements (at least in part) and you must review them.

8.2.3.2 (No subclause title)

You must keep a record of the review of product requirements. This record can be a signature, initials, stamp, form, or any other simple indicator. It's often affixed directly to the order or contract. Personnel working within the system should understand what constitutes the record of review and what it represents. Simply having a copy of the order or contract doesn't constitute a record of its review.

8.2.4 Changes to requirements for products and services

Orders and contracts are rarely static. They often evolve and change during the course of their lives. When product requirements change, make sure to amend the relevant documents. These could include work orders, travelers, specifications, schedules, or other documents. Failure to amend these documents can have huge negative consequences. In addition to amending relevant documents, you must have a system for communicating the changes to people who need to know. The communication can take place through the amended documents or through other means such as meetings, telephone calls, and e-mails.

Always remember this important bottom line: *If you can't meet the requirements, don't accept the order.* Customers will only take their business elsewhere if you commit to things you can't accomplish. Even worse, they will tell their friends and colleagues that you make promises you can't keep.

8.3 DESIGN AND DEVELOPMENT OF PRODUCTS AND SERVICES

8.3.1 General

Equivalent to clause 7.3 in ISO 9001:2008.

This section of the standard addresses the design of your products and services. It doesn't specifically address design of an internal process, although the requirements could certainly be applied to that type of activity. At a minimum, you must meet the requirements in the design of products if you perform design. Many organizations determine this requirement to be "not applicable" because they simply fulfill customer requirements and no design is performed.

Before you happily declare, "We don't do design!" let's discuss it a little further. Here are some criteria for deciding if you are actually designing and developing:

- If you are producing a unique product or service for which your customer hasn't provided specifications, you may be doing design and development.
- If your customer has only given you vague performance requirements and asked you to come up with a product or service that will meet those requirements, you may be doing design and development.
- If your product is driven by your organization's powers of creativity and innovation, you may be doing design and development.
- If one or more of your products is protected by patents, you may be doing design and development.

Clearly, there are exceptions to each of these cases. The good news is that design and development can be very simple. In essence, it's nothing more than project management: breaking a complex process into more manageable activities. Let's examine each of the steps and explain what they require.

8.3.2 Design and development planning

The design plan is the path you expect to take in creating the design. Given your knowledge of the product's complexity, what tasks will need to be involved? Who will need to take part and how long will the process take? What resources will be needed? The design plan will be your road map for the remainder of the process.

The plan can take many forms, from highly sophisticated to very simple. ISO 9001:2015 states that planning must consider the nature, duration, and complexity of the design-and-development activities. This means that the design plan for a manned space rocket is going to be much different than a design plan for a plastic toy. The trick is to match the design plan to the nature of the product being designed. Some design plans are little more than a memo or a flow diagram. For more complex products, the design plan may comprise many documents, including a Gantt chart, critical path, work breakdown structure, and other project management tools. ISO 9001:2015 doesn't explicitly require the design plan to be maintained as documented information, but it would be difficult to communicate and manage without it being documented.

Only use as much planning as you need. Remember, the purpose of design planning is to help you manage the design process, and there's no extra credit for being fancy or using complicated tools. The way you achieve design planning is completely up to you. Your design plan will typically address a number of variables:

- *Duration of the project.* When does the design start, and when do you hope to have it finished? Does the expected duration match the nature and complexity of the design?
- *Design stages.* What major tasks must be performed to produce the design? In what sequence should these tasks be performed? Design reviews— where you review progress and address obstacles—must also be planned.
- *Verification and validation.* Verification is where you check the design outputs against design inputs. Validation is where you check the design under conditions of actual use. Both of these must be planned.
- *Responsibilities and authorities.* Who will be involved with this design? What will they be expected to do, and what do they have the authority to do? Do the participants understand and accept their responsibilities?

- *Resources.* What funds, facilities, equipment, supplies, and other resources will be needed to complete this design? Have the resources been secured? If not, where will they come from? Make sure to address resources from internal sources, as well as external sources.
- *Interfaces.* With whom should the persons with design responsibilities interface or interact? Nobody works in isolation (or at least they shouldn't), and it's important to drive as much communication and interaction as possible.
- *Involvement of customers and users.* Not all designs require the involvement of customers and users, but this kind of interaction must be carefully planned when needed. Many consumer products make use of customers and users at various stages of design.
- *Requirements for production.* You must plan for how the design might affect other parts of the organization. Are there safety issues that must be considered? Are there environmental issues? Are there implications for packaging, storage, and transportation?
- *Level of control.* It's safe to assume that the organization will be expected to have primary control over its design process. There may be certain aspects of design outside the organization's control. It's possible that customers and interested parties may have certain roles to play in design, such as participating in design reviews, design verifications, and validations. The levels of control and responsibility for all activities should be defined during the planning process.
- *Documented information needed to demonstrate requirements have been met.* During planning, you must determine which documents and records will be needed during the design process.

For some organizations, the design plan is basically the same each time they design something. It's a routine process, with the only difference being the specific timing of the tasks. Organizations that design variations of the same kind of product often fall into this category. In these cases, there's no reason to make the design plan any more complicated than it needs to be. A simple template with spaces for the dates to be filled in works very well.

8.3.3 Design and development inputs

Inputs tell us what design and development must satisfy. The inputs may come from market research, customer feedback, sales reports, or pure speculation. Regardless of the source, ISO 9001:2015 outlines five areas that must be included as inputs:

- *Functional and performance requirements.* How should the product function? What must it be able to do? What resources must be available to support it? What are the product's limitations?
- *Information from previous designs.* There is a chance that your organization has designed a similar good or service in the past. Apply lessons learned in the earlier design to the current project.
- *Statutory and regulatory requirements.* What laws govern the production and use of your product? Are there any regulatory guidelines related to your product? How do these issues affect the design process?
- *Standards or codes.* These might include internal requirements and industry standards to which the organization subscribes.
- *Potential consequences of failure.* If we failed to accurately identify all the design inputs—or failed to execute the inputs—what bad things could happen? This is risk analysis applied to the design process itself.

Design inputs are often captured in meeting minutes, memos, design worksheets, market summaries, and sometimes on cocktail napkins. Wherever they are captured, they must be complete, unambiguous, and reviewed for adequacy. As part of this review, inputs should be analyzed for requirements that conflict with one another. Any conflicts in design inputs would need to be resolved. The design inputs are considered by ISO 9001:2015 to be retained documented information (i.e., records), as they indicate what the organization required at a particular time.

8.3.4 Design and development controls

This subclause of ISO 9001:2015 combines a number of separate activities into a single element. This is where the requirements for design review, design verification, and design validation now live. A number of controls are listed here:

- Results to be achieved are defined. The objectives of the design are the design inputs, which we discussed in the previous section.
- Design reviews are conducted.
- Verification activities are conducted.
- Validation activities are conducted.
- Actions are taken on problems discovered during review, verification, or validation. The whole purpose of these activities is to verify that you're meeting design requirements. If you fail to meet requirements, then action is certainly necessary.
- Documented information of all these activities is retained. Records must be kept of reviews, verifications, and validations.

Design review, verification, and validation are potentially complex processes. For many organizations, they warrant more than a one sentence explanation. Let's talk about each one of these in more detail.

Design and development review

Design reviews are the way you make sure the design is proceeding according to plan. All designs have at least one design review, and complex designs may have many more. There's no particular magic to the number of design reviews. If the design process has significant complexity and risk, there will need to be more design reviews. One of the key planning activities is to decide how many design reviews are appropriate for the particular product being designed.

Purposes of design review

There are two primary purposes of the design review:
- Evaluate the ability of the results of design and development to meet requirements.
- Identify any problems and propose necessary actions.

The design review is a reality check to ensure that everything is on track. If it's not, it will be revealed at the design review and appropriate action can be taken to fix the problem before it throws the entire project off schedule.

Design reviews must be action-oriented to be effective. ISO 9001:2015 also requires records of design reviews and any resulting actions.

Participants in design review

Participants in design reviews are those involved in the design stage being reviewed. Typical participants include designers, engineers, production managers, purchasing personnel, and logistics managers. Later in the design process, reviews may also include marketing, sales, and senior management. The point is to get the people who understand the variables of design together and review the status of all the design tasks. The design review doesn't have to be a physical meeting. It could be performed via teleconference or through other remote means. As long as the participants have access to necessary information relating to design progress, it doesn't really matter if everyone is together in the same room. Face-to-face dialogue can be helpful, however, especially when problems must be resolved.

Typical agenda

Each design review should be conducted according to a structured agenda. Don't leave the content of the design review up to the participants' discretion. Publish the agenda in advance and make sure all participants are prepared to contribute. This isn't a requirement of ISO 9001:2015, but it sure makes the review go smoother.

The following actions are typically addressed during a design review:

- Evaluate progress on the design.
- Compare progress against the design plan.
- Agree on actions needed to close gaps.
- Identify resources to be procured or realigned.
- Revise the design plan, if necessary.
- Provide feedback and encouragement to designers.
- Identify risks and roadblocks that have appeared, and decide how they will be managed.
- Confirm that the design is ready to move to the next stage.
- Ensure that the design stays focused on the design inputs.

Design and development verification

Design verification ensures that the design outputs meet the design inputs. It's basically an inspection activity, but one of the most critical inspection activities an organization can perform. Verification may be performed once near the end of the design process or it may be done at multiple times as incremental design outputs are generated. It all depends on the nature of the product being designed. Complex products will almost always require more than one design verification.

Verification topics

ISO 9001:2015 doesn't provide much guidance on what should be covered during design verification. It simply says that you should ensure outputs meet input requirements. Your inputs could cover nearly anything relevant to the product being designed. Here are some topics that could be addressed during design verification:

- *Confirmation of basic attributes.* This is the most routine type of verification. It involves a comparison of the requirements shown on design inputs against the attributes reflected on the output documents. Attributes that could be verified in this manner include size, shape, weight, color, and configuration.

- *Verification of performance properties.* This is a much more robust type of verification. Performance properties may include speed, strength, hardness, durability, reliability, and many other qualities. These properties typically can't be checked off in a mechanical fashion like basic attributes; calculations, simulations, or computer modeling may need to be utilized to know whether the performance requirements in the inputs have been satisfied by the outputs. Remember that these performance properties are shown on design output documents.

- *Tests of prototypes.* Design outputs sometimes include prototypes of the product being designed. In these cases, verification may include actual tests of the prototype's physical properties. We've now moved away from verifying documents to verifying something that the customer would recognize as a real product. The way the prototype differs from a real product is that it's not produced under typical production conditions. The prototypes are produced under careful conditions probably unlike those that will be present when the design goes into full production. Testing the prototype can still provide valuable insights.

- *Comparison to similar designs from the past.* History is a powerful source of knowledge, but it's often overlooked. When verifying design outputs, it's helpful to refer to earlier designs that have similar attributes and performance properties. How well does the current design shape up to designs of the past? Have we incorporated all the lessons learned from the earlier designs? Do we have customer feedback on earlier designs that needs to be incorporated into the current design?

- *Safety and health review.* Verification should carefully consider the safety and health aspects of the product being designed. The design inputs will provide direction on the applicable considerations, but sometimes it's difficult early in the process to know with certainty what safety and health issues apply. For that reason, design verification should apply a wide-ranging evaluation of all possible safety and health issues to ensure that nothing has been neglected. Unsafe or unhealthy products will doom the organization, no matter how innovative its products are.

- *Environmental impact review.* Every product used or produced has an environmental impact. It's a truth that's beyond argument. The question is not whether the new product causes environmental impacts, but their severity. The design outputs must be verified to ensure that they meet all applicable environmental laws. Just as important, the outputs should be verified to ensure that unregulated impacts aren't being generated in excess quantities. A full life-cycle review of the product, its packaging, and the associated supplies is a robust way to verify the environmental impact of the product being designed.

- *Marketing review.* Nearly everything mentioned so far about design verification has been technical in nature. However, we can't lose sight of the whole purpose of design: to meet a need in the marketplace. The organization's marketing specialists should be involved in the design verification to ensure that nothing identified in the design inputs is forgotten, particularly in the case of subtle or highly nuanced requirements.

- *Legal review.* In the United States, a company can be sued for almost anything. Grounds for filing suit range from the gravely serious to the ridiculous. The very nature of a new or improved product means that the organization is venturing into a potentially risky and untried operation. Many product designs require legal staff to be involved in the verification process so that these risks are properly managed.

Responsibility for performing verifications

Design verification can be performed by any qualified persons, inside or outside the organization. However, due to the confidential nature of most designs, verifications are typically performed inside the organization. Regardless of where verifications take place, it's helpful if the verification is performed by an independent function. At the very least, avoid having designers verify their own work.

Changes to the design

There is always the chance that design verification will result in changes to the design. That's really the point: to ensure the design is meeting all requirements, and, if not, to make necessary changes. Changes can be triggered by any number of factors:

- Failure to address input requirements
- Misinterpretation of input requirements
- Unsatisfactory test or simulation results
- Errors or omissions in the design
- Addition of lessons learned from earlier designs
- Unanticipated or unmet safety/health considerations
- Unanticipated or unmet environmental considerations
- Significant legal risks
- Addition of improved features or performance attributes

Records of design verification

Design verification always produces records. These records typically indicate who performed the verification, when it was performed, what specific parameters were verified, the results of the verification, and any actions that must be taken. The records can be quite simple, and often can be incorporated into other design records.

Design and development validation

Validation is similar to verification, except in the case of validation we no longer evaluate abstract representations of the product (e.g., drawings and specifications). Instead, we evaluate an actual version of the product itself. The product may be a production prototype, sample, beta test, pilot run, or first article, but essentially it's the same product that will be offered to customers. Validation sums up everything about the designed product and asks, "Will this product do everything it's supposed to do in the eyes of the customer?"

Design validation is one of the most important activities in the design control process. Why? Because it forces the organization to perform a reality check on its design work. It requires a deliberate, head-to-head examination of what the organization designed vs. the customer's use in the real world. Spend the time and effort to perform a comprehensive design validation.

Keys to successful validation

These are the four keys to successful validation:
- Evaluating the same product that customers will actually consume
- Evaluating the product in the same way customers will use or misuse it
- Evaluating the product in a holistic or cumulative manner, instead of only focusing on product attributes in isolation from one another
- Evaluating the production process to ensure it's truly capable of producing the new product

Don't make the mistake of validating a product that was produced by experts under carefully controlled conditions in a research-and-development laboratory. The validated product needs to be produced in the same way a product is produced for market consumption. All the typical production problems that arise when a product goes into day-to-day production should be considered. The organization shouldn't cherry pick its best materials, personnel, and equipment when producing a product for validation. The production conditions must be realistic.

Meeting requirements for specified application or intended use

Not only must the product be produced under realistic conditions, it must also be evaluated under realistic conditions. For example, if we're designing golf carts, we'll take a cart for a spin on an actual golf course. Rain, shine, hot, and cold, just as a real golfer might. The organization also needs to try to anticipate ways the customer might misuse the product. Perhaps the golf cart isn't really intended to be driven through three inches of standing water, but that's exactly what golfers will do. Golfers may also be expected to spill drinks on the seats and the dashboard. They may try to drive the cart over curbs and other obstructions. Validation needs to include all of these uses and misuses.

Of course, validation evaluates individual product features, but, more importantly, it must summarize all the features and determine if the product as a whole meets requirements. Everyone has heard the old cliché, "More than the sum of its parts." The words are accurate, cliché or not. The designed product is much more than the sum of its parts, and the validation should acknowledge this reality. The overall perceptions of the people performing validation are often more valuable than the results of individual evaluations.

The nature of design validation will differ drastically, depending on the product. Here are some examples of how different products may undergo validation:

- *Pharmaceuticals:* clinical trials
- *Educational courses:* beta tests using volunteer students
- *Automobiles:* road test trials, crash test trials, engineering tests
- *Food and beverages:* consumer taste tests, laboratory tests
- *Kitchen appliances:* multiple-cycle usage tests, consumer focus groups

Completed prior to the delivery or implementation of the product

Ideally, the organization should validate the design of its products before releasing them to the market, but sometimes this isn't possible. Certain products can't be validated under use conditions without getting the customer involved. This is especially the case for large, custom-designed products created for very specific applications. Whatever arrangement allows you to simulate "specified application or intended use" is what you will use, and this may require validation in the open market.

Records of validation

Just like verification, validation produces records. The records should outline all the details of the validation: the manner of validation, the conditions under which it took place, exactly what features or attributes were validated, who performed it, and when it took place. The typical rules of records apply here: Keep them simple and as concise as possible.

8.3.5 Design and development outputs

Design output is the product of the design process. The design output defines exactly what the organization will produce to meet the design input requirements. The output takes the input and turns it into something your organization can provide. Design output always takes the form of documentation of some sort. Here are some examples:

- Sketches
- Engineering drawings
- Blueprints
- Product specifications
- Service instructions
- Bills of materials
- Manufacturing instructions
- Installation instructions
- Specifications for components, subassemblies, raw materials, or other purchased products
- Packaging and labeling specifications
- Handling and storage specifications
- Appearance standards
- Safety warnings, labels, and reminders
- Consumer or user instructions
- Troubleshooting and repair guides
- Flowcharts
- Calculations
- Computer code
- Operating criteria
- Physical specimens or prototypes

The format and style of design outputs are only limited by the organization's imagination. Regardless of what the design outputs look like, there are a number of requirements the organization must meet:

- *Satisfy inputs.* The whole point of design output is to guide the organization in producing a new or improved product. To do this, the outputs must clearly meet the input requirements. This is very valuable, as it ensures that the organization keeps its eyes on the expectations of its customers and the marketplace as it goes through the design process.

- *Provide information for subsequent processes.* Design outputs are communication tools. Their primary function is to tell everyone what to do to make a new product successful. As such, they must provide information to functions such as purchasing, logistics, production, quality assurance, and sales. That's one of the reasons there may be multiple design outputs: They're tailored to a wide variety of functions.

- *Contain or reference verification and acceptance criteria.* The outputs must indicate what constitutes the acceptable attributes of the product. In other words, what specific requirements must the product meet? Examples of acceptance criteria may include dimensional tolerances, performance specifications, material properties, aesthetic requirements, and a wide range of other possible issues. The nature of the product clearly dictates what kind of acceptance criteria will apply. Note that acceptance criteria not only applies to the design of goods but also to services that the organization designs.

- *Specify characteristics for safe and proper use.* Customers are often very creative in the way they use products, especially new products. Occasionally, they even use products in ways that could lead to injury or death. The design outputs must clearly indicate the safe and appropriate use of the product. Doing this protects the organization and its customers. Organizations that have failed to perform this step with due diligence often find themselves facing costly lawsuits, bankruptcy, and criminal prosecution.

Finally, ISO 9001:2015 states that the organization will retain documented information on design outputs. The fact that we're asked to "retain" them means that these are records. Are design outputs—which are typically specifications of some sort—actually records? Of course not. They're documents because they are subject to change. Despite this error on the part of ISO 9001:2015, you should control design outputs like you would any other document: with approval, revision status, and all the other hallmarks of document control.

Design outputs logically lead to the next stage of design control, which is design review.

8.3.6 Design and development changes

This clause is applicable if your organization alters existing designs. When we change existing designs, we must perform many of the activities used in the original design. ISO 9001:2015 requires organizations to identify, review, and control (verify and validate) design change. In other words, design changes basically have to go back through the entire design process.

ISO 9001:2015 is very specific about what documented information must be retained (i.e., records) related to design changes:

- *Design changes.* Describe exactly what is changing about the design. Provide the background on the design change. Even though design planning isn't specifically required on design changes, this would be a good place to define timeframes and milestones related to the change.
- *Design reviews.* Just like any design, a change must undergo at least one review. Retain information on the participants, dates, issues discussed, and actions to be taken.
- *Authorization of changes.* Changes don't just happen. They are proposed, explored, and authorized. Make sure that you retain information on who authorized the design change and when it occurred. It's also a good idea to include justification for the change.
- *Actions to prevent negative effects.* Change, no matter how seemingly harmless, always has a ripple effect. How could other features and properties of the product be affected, and what are you doing to prevent adverse effects? Be specific and action oriented.

8.3 FREQUENTLY ASKED QUESTIONS

Do we need to keep separate records of each stage of design? We would like to combine all of these into a single record, sort of like a "design traveler" that follows a new product through the entire design process.

You can format your design records in whatever way makes sense to you. The record you described sounds like it could work very well.

8.4 CONTROL OF EXTERNALLY PROVIDED PROCESSES, PRODUCTS, AND SERVICES

8.4.1. General

Equivalent to subclause 7.4.1 of ISO 9001:2008.

ISO 9001:2015 took a perfectly clear and simple title (purchasing) and turned it into "externally provided processes, products, and services." Despite the bloated title, we're still talking about products and services you buy from other organizations. In a word, "purchasing." ISO 9001:2015 provides guidance on the types of purchases that will be addressed by this section. At minimum, three categories of purchases must be managed and controlled through your purchasing process:

- *Raw materials.* Any materials or components that actually become part of your products or services must be managed through your purchasing process.

- *Products or services that a supplier provides directly to your customer.* These are products and services that you sold, but somebody else actually provided. Examples include private-label products, drop-shipped items, and outsourced services. Once the order is taken, your organization is potentially out of the loop, so it's important that you exert some kind of control over the process.

- *Processes provided by subcontractors.* This is another way of saying outsourcing. Your organization is still involved in producing the product or service, but some aspect of it is provided externally. Examples might include a catering service that provides meals to corporate events. The catering service does the cooking, but sometimes they rely on an external delivery service to get the food to the customer location. Another example would be a manufacturing company that builds machinery. The company doesn't have painting equipment, so it relies on an outside firm to apply the paint. Both of these are examples of outsourcing.

Beyond these three categories, it's up to your organization to define the purchased products that have the most effect on your operations. Additional purchases that are considered "critical"—and which are managed through the purchasing requirements of ISO 9001:2015—include:

- Product packaging
- Equipment used to provide a service
- Mission-critical spare parts
- Outsourced testing labs that verify your product
- Transportation providers that deliver your goods or services
- Calibration services
- Providers of contract labor

Criteria for evaluation and selection

Evaluating and selecting external providers is a fairly straightforward task. Think about what drives your purchasing decisions when you're using your own money. The same criteria make sense for your company. Here are some common-sense selection factors:

- *Capability.* Does the external provider provide the type of product you're seeking? Are all necessary services, warranties, and information provided also? If not, there's no sense in investigating the supplier further.
- *Availability.* Can the external provider provide the good or service in the time and location desired?
- *Pricing.* Is the price competitive, given the total package of services offered? It's important to note that the lowest price is often not the best deal.
- *Quality.* Can the external provider meet your specifications, tolerances, and performance requirements?

- *Solvency.* Will the external provider still be in business next month? How about next year? This isn't necessarily a consideration for commodity items but is generally a requirement when warranties and product follow-up are part of the deal. You don't want to find a padlock on the supplier's door when you need technical assistance.
- *Implementation of a QMS.* A QMS is simply good management. Why not give preference to external providers that see value in a proactive approach to running their organizations? A formal management system will ensure a degree of customer focus, discipline, and problem prevention. If the supplier's management system has been registered by an accredited third party, this provides one more degree of oversight.

These are the most basic issues for selecting an external provider, and they are typically verified through research of sales literature, websites, published specifications, discussions with its representatives, industry journals, and customer references. Occasionally, the selection criteria may be verified through a trial purchase. This is the case when long-term contracts, large product quantities, or extremely critical products are involved. The trial purchase can reveal a great deal about what to expect over the long term.

Monitoring performance of external providers

Once you select suppliers and establish the relationship, you have to monitor their performance. Nearly any reasonable criteria can be used. The trick is applying meaningful measures that help you manage suppliers and improve their performance. The criteria for monitoring external providers can be intertwined with your verification of the product they provide. In many ways, this is the most meaningful way to evaluate external providers. Here are some typical performance monitoring criteria:

- *Timeliness.* Did the good or service arrive when it was supposed to?
- *Quantity.* Did the correct quantity arrive?
- *Location.* Did the good or service arrive at the correct location?
- *Identification.* Did the correct type of good or service arrive?
- *Condition.* Did the product arrive in the correct condition, with no damage or deterioration?

- *Achievement of requirements.* Did the good or service meet all the terms of the contract or order?
- *Test/inspection data.* Did the product arrive with the necessary test or inspection results, and do the results indicate that the product meets the requirements? (This may not be applicable to all products.)
- *Internal test results.* Does the product pass our internal tests or lab analyses? (This may not be applicable to all products.)
- *Performance.* Does the good or service perform satisfactorily in its intended application?
- *Billing.* Did the bill arrive when it was supposed to, and was it accurate?
- *Effectiveness.* Did the service accomplish what it was supposed to?
- *Courtesy.* Was the service person courteous?
- *Communication.* Was the service person or supplier representative able to communicate effectively?
- *Problem solving.* Was the service person or supplier representative able to diagnose and solve any problems?

Supplier auditing is occasionally promoted as a technique for evaluating and managing external providers. When performed correctly, auditing sends a powerful message to the external provider and can drive significant improvements. However, it brings with it many obstacles, such as:

- *Expense.* It's expensive to perform audits. Travel costs alone make this prohibitive for many organizations.
- *Difficulty.* Think how difficult it is for your internal auditors to audit your own facility and draw valid conclusions. It's exponentially more difficult to audit someone else's facility and draw valid conclusions and drive improvements. Only the most experienced and skillful auditors can succeed in supplier audits.
- *Logistics.* The logistics of trying to schedule audits is very complex. Agreeing on the date, time, scope, and agenda for an audit can take hours of back-and-forth communication between the organization and the supplier. Agreeing on how corrective actions will be handled is even more complex.
- *Intrusiveness.* External providers are busy. Just like your organization, they barely have time in the day to take care of the most pressing issues. Being

audited only constrains them further. Many external providers resent this intrusion and will bear it only grudgingly.

If auditing is considered valuable, then compel suppliers to develop their own internal auditing functions. Even more desirable is to require that they work toward the development of a formal management system with the ultimate goal of recognition by a third-party registrar. This allows the external provider to be the master of its destiny, and it also lowers the costs and aggravations of supplier management. In cases where the benefits of auditing suppliers outweigh the obstacles, dedicate the time and energy into making sure it achieves the desired results. Don't approach the task lightly.

Reevaluating suppliers

The final task is to define is the criteria for reevaluating external providers. This can be confusing. Reevaluation is the reconsideration of your organization using a particular supplier. In other words, it's clobbering time! Reevaluation is nearly always triggered by something bad that the supplier did. If you have meaningful criteria for evaluating external providers, then you'll know very quickly when they do something bad. Some situations that might trigger reevaluation include:
- Repeat problems
- Blatant disregard of your requirements
- Unprofessional conduct by the supplier
- Over-billing
- Failure to follow statutory or regulatory requirements
- Criminal prosecution
- Negative news reports

When you reevaluate an external provider, you decide if you want to continue the business relationship. It's a very serious decision. What criteria are useful for reevaluating external providers? Here are some typical ones:
- *Corrective action.* Issue the external provider a corrective action request, demanding investigation and action within a fixed time period. Failure to respond puts it at risk for losing its contract.

- *External provider audit.* Another way of reevaluating external providers is to audit their operations. We've already talked about the challenges of auditing suppliers, but it can be an effective practice when faced with the decision of continuing the business relationship. When problems are identified during the audit, the external provider is issued corrective action requests and its responses are carefully monitored.
- *Probation.* A third way of reevaluating external providers is to simply put them on "probation" within your purchasing system. Probation will usually subject them to reduced business and higher scrutiny for a length of time. If their performance improves during the probationary time, they will be removed from probation and reinstated as a normal supplier. If their performance does not improve during the probationary period, they are no longer used.

Retain documented information (i.e., keep records)

ISO 9001:2015 requires records of the following:
- Evaluation and selection of external providers
- Monitoring performance of external providers
- Reevaluation of external providers
- Any necessary actions

Records for these activities can vary widely. Here are some guidelines for effective records:
- *Incorporate them into existing paperwork.* If you already use a purchase order, incorporate your supplier evaluation into this tool. I have seen stickers, stamps, and other simple records used directly on the purchase order to indicate that the supplier was evaluated and how it performed against the criteria. Packing lists, receiving logs, and work orders can also be used to capture the evaluation.
- *Use automated digital records whenever possible.* If you have a computer system that receives purchased product, use this to record your supplier evaluation. Even if you don't have an automated system, a simple spreadsheet can record the details.

Both of these approaches are aimed at making the records as transparent as possible. If the creation of records is complex and time consuming, you can bet it won't happen.

8.4.2 Type and extent of control

Equivalent to subclauses 7.4.1 and 7.4.3 of ISO 9001:2008.

This element requires a serious analysis of how external providers affect your success and what you intend to do about it. The first requirement is just a blanket statement saying that external providers cannot adversely affect your ability to deliver conforming products. Everything else in this section builds on that blanket statement with progressing degrees of detail. Here are each of the requirements:

- *Ensure control within the QMS.* ISO 9001:2015 requires that purchasing remain within the control of the QMS. This is a rather obvious statement, as there are explicit requirements for purchasing in the standard that we're trying to meet.

- *Define the controls applied to suppliers and the resulting output.* These are two separate controls. The first is focused on the external provider itself. Will you audit the external provider, establish goals for performance, or track responsiveness? The second half of the requirement focuses on what the external provider provides. Will you inspect the product, test it in a laboratory, or survey customers? Every situation is obviously different. As long as the controls make sense and are fully implemented, they should be adequate. We discussed many of the controls you might choose in the previous section, under "performance monitoring."

- *Consider the effect on customers and statutory and regulatory requirements.* This effect should be part of the calculus used to determine the control you apply. For example, if the external provider has the ability to get your company in big trouble with a regulatory agency, then you would certainly want to apply much more control to that supplier. In the same vein, if the supplier has direct contact with your customers, you would also want to control them more for that reason. Examine the potential effect and provide appropriate controls.

Some organizations see fit to introduce even more selection criteria, including:

✓ Environmental performance
✓ Minority ownership
✓ Diversity of the work force
✓ Safety practices
✓ High ethical standards
✓ Overall working conditions
✓ Use of child labor
✓ Employee harassment and abuse
✓ Freedom of association for employees

These criteria address a category that I will call public relations and organizational values. It's a difficult category for most organizations to evaluate. The organization is really trying to answer two simple questions:

✓ Will the external provider's business practices expose the organization to negative public relations, possibly leading to risk or liability (such as negative media reports, civil lawsuits, or criminal prosecution)?
✓ Are the external provider's business practices so contrary to our own values that we cannot in good conscience enter into a relationship with it?

- *Consider the effectiveness of external providers' controls.* You can't control the external provider all by yourself. The external provider has to have internal controls. The more robust and proactive its controls are, the better prepared it will be to serve you. This requirement asks you to evaluate how well the external provider monitors itself. Are there strong internal controls or weak internal controls? The answer to this question will also influence how much control you will apply to the external provider. It bears repeating that the establishment of a QMS goes a long way toward making internal controls more effective.

- *Determine verification activities.* One of the most common-sense ways to manage external providers is through the verification of their output. When their products show up at your company, inspect them. When they perform a service on your behalf, check their effectiveness. Different products will be subject to different levels of verification. For example, office supplies can be verified through checking for correct quantity, identification, damage, and on-time delivery. More critical products—such as raw materials that go into a final product—might undergo lab tests, detailed visual inspection, and examination of statistical data. Services are likewise verified to ensure that they met requirements. All of these verifications must result in retained information (i.e., records). The records can be quite simple. In the case of the simple check of quantity, identification, and condition, the record could be the inspector's signature and date on the packing slip or receiving ticket. In the case of lab tests, the resulting test data would serve as the record of verification.

8.4.3 Information for external providers

Equivalent to subclause 7.4.2 of ISO 9001:2008.

This very simple subclause of ISO 9001:2015 is written so that it appears very complex. Here's the simple version: Tell your external providers exactly what you want from them. I told you it was simple. If you have a purchase order process, then it probably already requires full descriptions of the goods or services requested, date needed, delivery location, price, billing terms, applicable specifications, and any other requirements. Even if you simply use emails to communicate requirements to external providers, this system can be effectively used. The purchasing information requirement would be difficult to meet without some sort of record of what you have requested, however. From a strictly business standpoint, you would certainly want a record of what you have requisitioned.

Ensure the adequacy of requirements prior to communication

This statement is clear: Ensure the adequacy of purchase requirements before communicating with external providers. This is a common-sense requirement, as smart people rarely communicate something before checking the message for completeness, accuracy, and clarity. That's all this requirement asks for. The only way to prove that you checked something is to maintain a record of having done it. With a purchase order, a signature is typically adequate proof of having ensured the adequacy of purchase requirements.

8.4 FREQUENTLY ASKED QUESTIONS

Can we evaluate our suppliers though a supplier question-naire?

Yes, but weigh the value of a questionnaire against other types of criteria. Questionnaires are often "pencil whipped" by suppliers and seldom reflect meaningful performance of the suppliers.

Do we have to keep records of verifying purchased product?

Yes. Records aren't specifically required in clause 8.4, but there would be no other way to demonstrate that the verification took place. Also, clause 8.6 requires records of all product releases, which would certainly include purchased product.

8.5 PRODUCTION AND SERVICE PROVISION

8.5.1 Control of production and service provision

Equivalent to subclauses 7.5.1 and 7.5.2 of ISO 9001:2008.

The essence of this part of the standard is process control. You must control the processes that produce your goods and services. Other parts of ISO 9001:2015 address processes in broader terms (see clause 4.4), but these requirements are focused squarely on production. The term "control" is very broad, but ISO 9001 provides some examples of control. The final decisions of which controls are applicable to your processes are up to you.

Availability of product and service specifications

Your products and services must meet certain requirements. Some of the requirements are internal to your organization and some are external. Determination and review of product requirements is discussed in subclauses 8.2.2 and 8.2.3. The applicable portions of these requirements are what you need to make available. Document and make available the product requirements in manner that works for you. In all likelihood, you already have specifications of some sort, especially if you manufacture products. Service providers also need to document the requirements related to their services and activities. Take an inventory of all applicable requirements—internal, customer-mandated, legally mandated, corporate-mandated—and make sure that these are addressed. Here are some of the most typical ways to make product information available:

- Specifications
- Drawings and blueprints
- Work orders
- Travelers
- Schedules
- Contracts
- Job folders
- Production tickets

The second part of this requirement asks you to make available "results to be achieved." This speaks to the performance properties of the product or service. What should the product be able to do, and how do you ensure it's capable? These types of requirements are usually documented within one of the specifications listed above. Results to be achieved also serve as a linkage to clause 8.6, Release of products and services. This is where you actually verify that your products and services meet all applicable requirements.

Availability and use of verification equipment

The planning of processes that you performed in clause 8.1 will also determine the monitoring and measuring devices you need. Whatever devices you determined as being necessary must be provided, and you must have methods for ensuring that the monitoring and measuring devices remain available. This topic is described in much more detail in subclause 7.1.5, Monitoring and measuring resources (formerly known as calibration). Keep in mind that you're not required to have monitoring and measuring devices; they're only necessary if your products, processes, or services require them to be effective.

Implementation of monitoring and measurement

This requirement is a basically a repeat of the one above it. Instead of just saying "use," this section says "implementation." The meaning is the same. If you commit to monitoring and measuring something, then you must do it. This clause also states that the purpose of implementing monitoring and measuring resources is to ensure that the criteria for processes, products, and services have been met. The only way to prove you have done this is by retaining documented information (i.e., maintaining a record) of the results of implementing monitoring or measurement.

Effective infrastructure and environment

This is a simple requirement. You're required to have equipment and an environment suitable to produce your goods or services. If the equipment or environment is unsuitable, you must take action to make it suitable. These types of issues are often handled through a maintenance program of some sort, whether maintenance is performed in-house or externally subcontracted. The determination of what constitutes suitable equipment and environment is generally determined during the planning processes described in clause 8.1. Infrastructure is discussed in more detail in subclause 7.1.3, and environment is discussed in more detail in subclause 7.1.4.

Selection of competent people

There are very few production operations that run without people. ISO 9001:2015 asks you to define the people necessary to conduct your production processes and to further define what makes them competent and qualified. You have likely already addressed this through clause 7.2, Competence. The present requirement is really just a placeholder to remind you to pay special attention to the competency and qualification needs of the people who actually make what you sell.

Validation of processes when outcomes cannot be verified

This requirement applies to very few organizations. Specifically, those organizations that produce a product or service that cannot be verified. In other words, you created a product, but you don't have any way of verifying it before it's consumed or used by the customer. Because this topic is somewhat esoteric, a full discussion of the requirements can be found in appendix B of this book.

Actions to remove human error

This is a new addition to ISO 9001:2015. Human error is an inevitable part of life. The objective of every organization, however, should be to make human error harder to happen. You want to "error-proof" your process. This is a significant part of lean manufacturing and the Toyota production system, and the subject of many books and management courses. It's also remarkably simple. Let's address a handful of actions that help to remove human error:

- *Assigning locations to tools and supplies.* The old adage, "A place for everything and everything in its place," is at least a hundred years old, but it's pure wisdom. Countless delays and mistakes take place because employees can't find what they need. Establish locations for tools, supplies, and visual materials (shadow boards, labeled shelves, colored bins, etc.), and then enforce the discipline of using the assigned location.

- *Forms and checklists.* Many years ago I worked in a textile company. The ladies in customer service took orders for fabric using a blank piece of paper. Consequently, it was a common occurrence to forget certain important details of the order. After all, they were using a blank piece of paper and they had to remember which details to ask for. We finally implemented a structured form for taking orders and the incidence of neglecting details went down to almost zero. Why? The form error-proofed the process. The customer service agents no longer had to rely on their memories; they just followed the flow of the form. Checklists that prescribe a sequence of checks or activities serve the same purpose. It's important to remember that forms and checklists can be hard copy or electronic.

- *Parceling out specific quantities.* Granny sometimes forgets to take her medicine. Other days, she takes twice her medicine. Why? Because the storage location is simply a bottle of pills, and there's no indicator to remind her of what she has taken. To error-proof this process, all of Granny's pills are put into a rectangular pill container that has a separate compartment for each day of the week. All Granny has to do is open up the compartment and take the pills for today. If the compartment is empty, then she has already taken her pills. This is a very simple example, but the applications are the same in any situation where a specific quantity of material is used in a process.

- *Emergency stops.* At the furniture shop, the owner Bob was noticing a lot of "near misses" on the circular saw. Workers would turn on the saw and then work dangerously close to the spinning blade as they aligned the wood to be cut. Bob called his electrician friend and asked if the saw could be modified so that it only turned on if a safety cover had been lowered over the blade. The electrician made the modification and included a feature that automatically turned off the saw if someone raised the safety cover. This is a typical example of error-proofing applied to a safety hazard.

- *Document control.* Who would ever think of document control as error-proofing? Well, that's exactly what it is. Document control is a process that ensures that only the most current information is available to employees. Obsolete information is removed so that it can't be accidently applied. Employees no longer have to wonder, "Is this the most current version of the specification?" The opportunity for making an error has been eliminated. So, if you have an effective document control process, you've already implemented an action to prevent human error.

- *Templates.* ACME Corp. had a customer that required a certain sticker to be placed on every box of product it purchased. Easy enough, except that the sticker had to be placed on the same side as the address label, in the upper right corner, 50 millimeters down from the top edge, and 75 millimeters from the side edge. These instructions confused employees, and the ACME's customers often rejected shipments because the stickers were in the wrong location. In order to error-proof the process, ACME's purchasing department bought boxes that already had a template (or outline) printed on them, showing exactly where the stickers needed to go. The problem of incorrect sticker placement went away immediately.

These are just a few examples of error-proofing. Examine your own processes and talk to employees. Ask them about errors and mistakes that could be easily avoided. They will probably give you dozens of examples. Modify the processes so that it becomes more difficult to make the mistake. Voila! You have now performed error-proofing.

Release, delivery, and post-delivery activities

Control must be established to ensure that you meet requirements for release, delivery, and post-delivery activities. The meaning of these words can be a little confusing. Release is how we know that a product (either a good or service) is ready to leave our direct control and be transferred to the customer. Delivery is how we actually transfer the product to the customer; in the case of a service, delivery is the performance of the service. Post-delivery might consist of installation, technical follow-up, troubleshooting, answering of questions, clarification of issues, or gathering of customer perceptions.

Control of production at I. Technical Services

Managing operations can be as simple as ringing a bell. That's the philosophy that I. Technical Services has taken in Alpharetta, Georgia. I. Technical Services (*www.itechserv.com*) performs electronic manufacturing services, including PCB assembly, system assembly, test engineering, repair, and logistics. They compete against low-cost companies in Asia and elsewhere, so they have to be as efficient and lean as possible. One of their most efficient processes for managing production is their "bell meeting." At 9:00 every morning the production supervisor rings a ship's bell that's mounted on the wall. All the managers and supervisors assemble under the bell for a meeting that lasts about 15 minutes. They discuss what is running that day, what needs to be shipped, and any obstacles or concerns. Important notes are recorded on a white dry-erase board right below the bell.

"Everybody leaves that meeting knowing exactly what needs to happen," says Hector Rivera, I. Technical Services' quality manager. "It's the best investment of 15 minutes you can imagine."

Throughout the day, employees refer to the production notes on the white board, keeping themselves focused on what was agreed to. They ring the bell again at 3:00 p.m. every day, and the key players once more gather around the bell. The focus of this later meeting is to get everybody caught up on the current status of production. Where are we right now? What's left to be done? Will we meet all of our commitments today? Resources are rearranged as needed, and last-minute roadblocks are removed.

General Manager Lauren Thompson summarizes the process by saying, "When we come together under the bell, we're not managers of different departments. We're a single team working to wow the customer. It reminds us why we're there in the first place."

I. Technical Services has conducted their bell meeting twice a day for years. It's a very simple, yet powerful process for controlling production.

8.5.1 FREQUENTLY ASKED QUESTIONS

ISO 9001:2015 doesn't even mention work instructions anymore. Does that mean this sort of tool isn't considered effective?

No, not at all. The fact that ISO 9001:2015 doesn't mention it reflects the general movement away from prescribing documentation. If you see value in work instructions, then by all means use them. Keep them graphic, concise, and located near the point of use.

8.5.2 Identification and traceability

There are few processes more basic than identification. Confusion over "What is this stuff?" has caused more problems and customer complaints than just about any other issue. When products lack identification, you can expect trouble. It pays to have everything clearly and positively identified in some way. The first sentence of this requirement includes the weasely words, "When it is necessary…" I can think of very few instances when it is *not* necessary to identify product. Perhaps in an environment where there's only one product being produced and it's readily identifiable by sight. This is a very rare example, however. In nearly every organization it will be necessary to maintain positive identification of all outputs: products, components, raw materials, processes, and services. The good news is that this is very easy to do. Here are some of the most common methods:

- Labels
- Stickers
- Tickets
- Bar codes
- Tags

- Serial numbers
- Travelers and work orders
- Radio frequency identification
- Container identification
- Location identification

It's worth taking note of the final two examples. You could identify products by placing them in containers or physical locations that are identified. The individual products might not be identified, but their identification is communicated by where they're stored.

Identify verification status

Nearly all outputs (i.e., products and services) must be checked in some way to verify conformance. You, your customers, and other parties establish requirements, and then you monitor and measure the product or service to make sure it meets the requirements. This part of ISO 9001:2015 asks you to make it clear to everyone whether the product has been monitored and measured and what the results were. Again, this is a fairly easy task. Here are some examples of how it can be achieved:

- Inspection results recorded on travelers or work orders that accompany the product
- Containers that indicate the inspection status of product inside
- Designated physical locations for products of different inspection status
- Test results maintained in a database that are traceable back to products by a serial numbers or bar codes
- Individual inspection sheets posted on or near the product
- Inspection checklists that are traceable back to the product
- Customer sign-off to indicate acceptance of the service

As long as you can explain your process of identifying output status—and there is evidence it works—then you should be in good shape.

When traceability is a requirement...

ISO 9001:2015 doesn't explicitly require traceability of your products. It simply says, "When traceability is a requirement..." So when is traceability a requirement? Generally, traceability will be required under any of the following conditions:

- You require traceability as an internal requirement.
- Your customers require traceability as a term of their order or contract.
- Statutory or regulatory requirements require traceability.

Traceability is being able to say exactly what went into the product. It enables us to know what raw materials and components were used, who the suppliers were, which personnel worked on the product, and which machines and equipment were used. It always involves unique identification, because generic identification won't enable the detail needed to trace the components of a product. For tangible goods, traceability often involves batch numbers, lot numbers, and other unique identifiers. For service, traceability might be indicating who performed the service, the date it was performed, and the location. Traceability can be indicated on travelers, work orders, or job sheets, among other places in manufacturing environments. In service environments, it can be through service orders, memos, and meeting minutes. The traceability will always involve two things: unique identifiers and retained documented information (i.e., records).

It's worth mentioning that there are actually two different types of traceability:

- *One-way traceability.* This is being able to trace backward from a product to all the things (raw materials, supplies, people, etc.) that produced it.
- *Two-way traceability.* This is being able to trace back to what went into a product and being able to trace forward to where the product went when it left your control.

In general, when the term "traceability" is used without any qualifiers, it's referring to one-way traceability. If your organization defines this differently, you might want to clarify the term somewhere within your documented information.

8.5.3 Property belonging to customers and external providers

Equivalent to subclause 7.5.4 of ISO 9001:2008, with the addition of supplier property.

Customer and external provider property includes a wide range of things that you use or process in some capacity, but which belong to somebody else. What kinds of things might fall into this category? Here are some of the most common:

- Raw materials
- Specialized equipment
- Measuring devices
- Products returned for repair or warranty work
- Molds and tooling
- Templates and patterns
- Jigs and fixtures
- Returnable containers
- Rack and shelves
- Vending machines
- Packaging and labeling
- Intellectual property
- Personal data on customer or supplier employees
- Access to customer or supplier premises or facilities

If you do use customer or external provider property of any description—and your customer or external provider has not explicitly transferred ownership of the property to your organization—you have a number of responsibilities as defined by ISO 9001:2015. They generically fall into the category of exercising care with the property. In fact, those are the exact words that are used. What are some specifics of "you will exercise care?" Here is the care that is required:

Identify property

Identification means marking the property in such a way that you know it belongs to your customer or external provider. This can be accomplished in wide variety of ways. The same methods mentioned in subclause 8.5.2, Identification and traceability, can be applied here.

Verify property

Verification means checking product upon arrival to make sure it is usable and correct. You probably already inspect incoming material as part of complying with clause 8.4, Control of externally provided processes, products, and services. The only difference is that you're unlikely to have a purchase order that communicates the requirements related to customer property. Establish a formal process of inspecting customer property and verify it for all applicable requirements.

Protect and safeguard property

"Protect" and "safeguard" mean basically the same thing. In practical terms, they mean keeping the property in good, usable condition while it's under your control. The property may require special environmental conditions, handling and storage procedures, operating conditions, or maintenance. You must agree with your customer or supplier about who will be responsible for them and how they will be performed.

Property that is lost, damaged, or found to be unsuitable

Hopefully, nothing bad happens to the property while it's in your control. However, just in case it does, you must establish a process for addressing it. If something happens to the customer or supplier property (e.g., it's lost, damaged, or broken), you must report the problem to the owner and have a record of the communication. In addition to being an ISO 9001:2015 requirement, it's a good idea from a business standpoint.

8.5.4 Preservation

Equivalent to subclause 7.5.5 of ISO 9001:2008.

Preservation of outputs is a broad topic, and its specifics may differ drastically from organization to organization. This is very short section of ISO 9001:2015 in which you define your own controls. Your responsibility for preservation starts at internal processing (i.e., at the time you formally accept product or materials) and continues until the product or service is delivered. Of course, you may hire subcontractors to perform delivery, but you're still responsible for their ability to preserve the product.

One of the easiest ways to think about preservation of a physical product is to apply the concept to the different phases of production: handling, packaging, storage, protection. When preservation applies to services, it often also follows these phases, since preservation really applies to physical resources of some sort.

Preservation during handling

Handling refers to the physical manipulation of the product. You must determine the correct handling for your product, given its inherent properties and customer requirements. As usual, this will differ widely, depending on your product. Here are some examples of handling requirements:

- Method for moving and transporting product
- Responsibilities for moving and transporting product
- Inspection requirements for transportation equipment
- Limitations related to dropping or shaking the product
- Loading patterns for shipping containers or truck trailers
- Handling sequence
- Handling designed to prevent electrostatic discharge (ESD)
- Approved shippers and transportation providers
- Hygiene requirements for personnel who handle product
- Special handling requirements for trademarked product

Preservation during packaging

Nearly all physical products (i.e., goods) require packaging of some sort. The purpose of the packaging is often a mix of product preservation and loss control. If you produce goods, you probably determined the right packaging for your products long ago. Failure to do so would be very costly in terms of claims and returned goods. What you may not do is periodically revisit the packaging requirements, based on customer feedback, changes in transportation, and changes in customer locations, etc. Determine the right packaging for your products and periodically revisit this in light of changing circumstances. It's also common for organizations to stipulate approved suppliers of packaging materials. Here are some examples of packaging requirements:

- Outer packaging
- Packaging graphics
- Inner packaging
- Labels and bar codes
- Shrink wrapping
- Information that personnel must record on packaging
- Documentation attached to packaging
- Requirements for packaging cleanliness
- Inspection of packaging prior to use
- Design of product packaging facilities
- Approved method of packaging disposal

Preservation during storage

The amount of product that's damaged in storage is staggering. In fact, I usually consider product in stock to be a liability as it stands such a strong chance of being damaged or compromised in some way. Nonetheless, organizations that produce goods usually have to store them before they're shipped. It's your organization's responsibility to determine the appropriate storage and protection of these products. This not only applies to product maintained on your property, but also to product within subcontractor warehouses and shipping facilities. You must consider the following environmental conditions when storing your product:

- Configuration of storage area
- Access to product
- Security requirements (closed circuit cameras, locked areas)
- Pest control requirements
- Housekeeping requirements
- Periodic inspection of products in stock
- Periodic inspection of grounds and facilities
- Location of refuse containers
- First-in, first-out (FIFO) requirements
- Monitoring of product to detect contamination

Where requirements related to identification, handling, packaging, and storage are necessary, they're typically documented in work instructions, product specifications, handling standards, checklists, visual reminders, and other means. ISO 9001:2015 doesn't require you to maintain documented information, but it certainly would be a good idea to preserve the product. If your product has any special requirements, strongly consider documenting your preservation procedures in a lean and concise manner.

8.5.5 Post-delivery activities

Equivalent to subclauses 7.5.1 and 7.2.1 in ISO 9001:2008.

So, you made the sale. You even delivered the product or service. That's the end of the story until the next time the customer wants to buy something again, right? Maybe not. Previous versions of ISO 9001 addressed post-delivery activities with no more than a handful of words. Now it represents its own subclause. The reason is that post-delivery activities strongly influence customer loyalty and future sales potential. Post-delivery activities help move a sale away from a simple transaction and toward a long-term relationship.

ISO 9001:2015 doesn't define which post-delivery activities might be appropriate. It's up to your organization to figure that out. The standard does ask you to consider a number of factors:

- *Statutory and regulatory requirements.* It's relatively rare that there are statutory or regulatory requirements for post-delivery activities. As with most government intrusion into business, the purpose is to mitigate some potentially ill effect that the product could have. An example of a post-delivery activity mandated by statutory or regulatory authorities could be disposal of used tires after their usable life. Certain states have very specific requirements for how used tires are to be handled, stored, and reported when they're received back from customers. If you have a product covered under statutory or regulatory requirements, your organization is probably well aware of these requirements.

- *Potential problems.* Perhaps you have a product that is easily misused. Maybe the product is quite safe with one application, but completely inappropriate and dangerous for another application. Or let's say that a certain quantity of your product is perfectly safe, but in excess the prod-

uct becomes dangerous. In both of these cases, there are potentially undesired consequences of your product or service that might motivate your
organization to take certain actions after delivery. These might involve
follow-up contacts to customers or public service announcements.

• *Application and lifecycle.* This is a broad category to consider, and it encompasses a wide range of situations that might apply. For instance, your
service might be refinishing floors in a multi-step process. After the initial delivery of the product, you might need to contact the customer to
schedule the second phase of work. Another example might be contacting customers after 30 days of product installation to make sure that
everything works properly. Or, you might be a pest control company that
contacts its customers once a year to re-initiate their service contract.

• *Customer requirements.* Obviously, customer requirements drive the majority of what you do. If the customer contact or purchase order requires
that you perform certain tasks after delivery of the product, then of
course you will treat these just like any other requirement. An example
could be a service contract that is part of the sale of an industrial machine. The contract requires your company to return to the customer on
a monthly basis and perform preventive maintenance tasks. Of all the
considerations for post-delivery activities, this one is the most clear-cut
because it's usually spelled out right in the purchase order, contract, or
statement of work.

• *Customer feedback.* Customer feedback ultimately is a key influencer of
your organization's products and services. Desire for post-delivery activities is often framed as, "Hey, it sure would be nice if your company did
XYZ." If the XYZ takes place after delivery of the product or service,
then it fits into this category. An example could be training that your organization performs at the customer location. Perhaps through customer
feedback, you've learned that the customer would like its people to be
trained on your product twice a year. If you're smart, you'll make this
part of your post-delivery value proposition, and it becomes one more
step toward customer loyalty.

None of these issues necessarily will require your organization to do anything. They are simply considerations to help guide you in knowing which

post-delivery activities will be appropriate. There is a direct link between this section of ISO 9001:2015 and subclause 8.2.2, Determining the requirements for products and services. The point being that post-delivery activities—when they apply—will become important documented information used at multiple stages of your operation.

8.5.5 FREQUENTLY ASKED QUESTIONS

Due to the nature of our business, we have no post-delivery activities. In fact, our customers don't want us to follow up with them for any reason. Do we have to specify post-delivery activities?

No, of course not. This is only applicable if it is needed to achieve product conformity or customer satisfaction.

8.5.6 Control of changes

Somewhat equivalent to subclauses 4.2.3 and 5.4.2 in ISO 9001:2008, but with new requirements.

ISO 9001:2015 already addressed change control in another clause: 6.3, Planning of changes. Why come up with an entirely different subclause to address the topic again? That's a very good question. The present subclause has a subtle difference that might have motivated an entirely different section, chiefly that the focus is on production. In other words, the changes that happen in the factory, at the service location, or at the office where we do our work. The changes that happen on this level are usually very tactical and their effects are felt almost immediately. We're not talking about change that will take months to implement. We're talking about change that will most likely be put into place today, with the effects being felt by our customers and employees very quickly. The overall flavor of this section seems to reinforce the idea of the organization being flexible and adaptable. When the need for changes arise, you're able to meet them head-on. The changes addressed here could be proactive (ahead of time) or reactive (after the fact), but there seems to be a bias toward reactive change.

Another significant difference is that this subclause requires you to retain documented information (i.e., keep records). The records will include:

- Results of reviewing the changes
- Who authorized the change
- Any necessary actions from the review

Each of these items is fairly straightforward, but we'll provide some direction on each one.

- *Results of changes.* What did the change do for us? Was it good or bad? What evidence tells us this? You won't know the results of changes until the changes have already been made. This is why I said earlier that there seemed to be a slight bias toward reactive change. A change was made with good intentions, but now the organization has to take a step backward and decide what it accomplished.
- *Who authorized the change.* Changes that happen on the production floor will most likely be authorized by someone with direct leadership over the process. This could be a supervisor, shift foreman, lead person, or senior operator. It's completely up to you who you designate as having the authority to authorize change. Because these changes happen quickly, you probably don't want to push the authorization too far up into the stratosphere. The higher you go in the organization, the slower the response time tends to be. Keep the authorization at the same level that the change affects. The proof of who authorized change could be accomplished by initials, signature, employee number, ID card scan, or keypad/keyboard entry.
- *Necessary actions from the review.* The two main decisions that would normally come out of the review are one of the following:
  - ✓ *Go back to the old way.* The change didn't have the intended effects and the original method was better. Make sure everybody knows that we're going back to the old way of operating the process.
  - ✓ *Establish the change as the new benchmark.* Formalize the change, revise applicable documents, train employees, communicate the change, etc.

Necessary actions from the review are important because this is the sustainability aspect of the change. Either we're going to go back to the old way, or we're going to leap forward to the new way. In either case, the decision is formal and deliberate, and the decision touches many other parts of your QMS.

The retained documented information (i.e., record) that comes out of the change doesn't need to be complicated. The simpler the better. The changes that happen in production are implemented quickly, so the records that result from them should be quickly generated. A simple form, logbook, spreadsheet, or database could easily capture the needed information. Over time, your organization is building a history of how your production process has evolved and improved. This will also be reflected in the documented information you maintain (e.g., production procedures), but control of changes provides an opportunity to tweak, adjust, and adapt, and then decide if these need to become formalized.

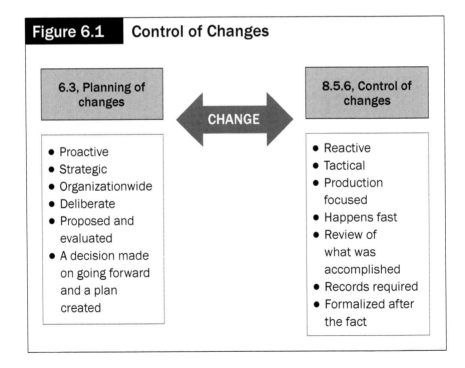

Figure 6.1   **Control of Changes**

6.3, Planning of changes

CHANGE

8.5.6, Control of changes

- Proactive
- Strategic
- Organizationwide
- Deliberate
- Proposed and evaluated
- A decision made on going forward and a plan created

- Reactive
- Tactical
- Production focused
- Happens fast
- Review of what was accomplished
- Records required
- Formalized after the fact

8.6 RELEASE OF PRODUCTS AND SERVICES

Equivalent to subclause 8.2.4 of ISO 9001:2008.

Before you release something, what should you do? You should check it. That's the underlying message of this part of ISO 9001:2015. A more descriptive title could have been "test, inspection, review, patrol, examination, and assessment," but the standard writers decided on the more mysterious term of "release." Release of conforming product or service is the ultimate goal of this section, but the magic is in the process that leads to this outcome. Exactly what that process looks like is completely up to you. It all depends on the requirements of the product or service that you're verifying.

- *Implement planned arrangements.* Like nearly everything else in ISO 9001:2015, your release processes are planned. That means they are determined ahead of time, resourced properly, and fully implemented. You would never walk out onto your shipping dock and say, "I wonder how we should inspect this product." Decisions like this are planned well in advance of having a product. The planned arrangements are also typically maintained as documented information (e.g., inspection procedures of some sort), though ISO 9001:2015 doesn't require it. Here are some monitoring and measurement details that are highly recommended for organizations to define:
  - ✓ *When does monitoring and measurement take place?* Define the timeframe or conditions that trigger verification.
  - ✓ *Who performs the monitoring and measurement?* Be specific about what function must perform or supervise the monitoring and measurement.
  - ✓ *What type of monitoring and measurement will be used?* Describe exactly what type of monitoring and measurement will take place.
  - ✓ *What measuring equipment is used?* This is an especially important aspect because measuring equipment usually requires calibration.
  - ✓ *What are the acceptance criteria?* In other words, what requirements does the product need to meet? These are sometimes referred to as specifications, tolerances, or standards.
  - ✓ *What records are created?* When product is monitored and measured, records are always created.

- *At appropriate stages.* When is the right time for you to monitor and measure your product? Only you know this, and it all depends on the product and your customer's requirements. You might verify your product multiple times during its production or just inspect it once at the end of the process. The numbers and magnitude of product verifications will depend on many factors, including:
  - ✓ *Complexity of the product.* The more complex the product, the more verifications it will usually require. A wider range of verifications may also be necessary.
  - ✓ *Magnitude of product requirements.* The more requirements that have been placed on the product by customers or the organization, the more verification steps that will be necessary.
  - ✓ *Ability to detect defects.* For some products, defects are concealed as the product progresses through the realization process. It makes sense to verify requirements while the defects are still detectable.

- *Verify that requirements have been met.* Yes, this is the whole point of checking your product or service. The range of verification methods for product or service is almost limitless. Whatever reveals the true conformity in the timeliest manner is what you need to implement. Here are a few of the most common ways to monitor and measure products or services:
  - ✓ Testing products in a lab
  - ✓ Automated monitoring by a machine
  - ✓ Operator inspection at the point of production
  - ✓ Sensory evaluation
  - ✓ Comparing the product or service against a standard
  - ✓ Soliciting customer feedback of services
  - ✓ Observation of a service against defined criteria
  - ✓ Subcontracted inspection and test services
  - ✓ Relying on test data from suppliers (in the case of purchased product)
  - ✓ Sampling inspection with a statistical sampling plan

- *Release of product and delivery of service shall not proceed until...* You must observe whatever product requirements that have been established. For example, you can't ship product that doesn't meet specifications. It's a no-brainer. Just abide by your procedures and specifications and make sure you have records that demonstrate that the product has met requirements. You can get around your product specifications if your customer or another relevant authority says it's OK. This is referred to as a "concession." Concessions must meet some general conditions:

✓ They are always recorded.

✓ They are always specific about what requirements are being waived.

✓ They provide clear traceability to the product that they concern (dates of production, batch, serial numbers, etc.) and the person authorizing the concession.

Concessions must always be granted by the customer if the requirement comes from the customer. In the event of internal product or service requirements, concessions can typically be granted by management.

• *Records of release.* Your organization must retain records of releasing products and services. These are some of the most important records you will ever generate because they indicate that you completed your inspection plan and that your product met the requirements. ISO 9001:2015 specifically requires two pieces of information to be captured as part of these records:

✓ *Evidence of conformity with acceptance criteria.* In other words, the results of your inspection or test. The records should clearly show that the products or services met the requirements. If the verification is visual, the results should describe what was observed. If the verification involved actual measurements, these should be recorded. Cryptic comments like "OK" don't provide much evidence of conformity.

✓ *Traceability to person(s) authorizing release.* This might be the person performing the verification or somebody with authority over the release process. In either case, we have traceability and accountability. In the event there are later problems with the product or service, we have the ability to investigate how the release was conducted and who enabled it.

Besides the two items that are required to be part of your release records, these are other typical pieces of information that organizations see value in retaining, as applicable:

✓ Identification of product

✓ Traceability of product (e.g., batch number, lot number, serial number)

✓ Date of release

✓ Who performed or supervised the verification

✓ Who released the product (if different from who performed the verification)

✓ The acceptance criteria that was applied

✓ The results from monitoring and measurement of product

✓ Clear indication of whether requirements were met

✓ Measuring equipment used

✓ Environmental conditions at the time the product was verified

8.6 FREQUENTLY ASKED QUESTIONS

We inspect our products, but the record of inspection is shipped with our products to the customer. Is that OK?

No, it's not OK. How are you going to demonstrate that the inspection took place without a record of some sort? Consider developing a process that enables you to provide data to your customers and maintain proof of required inspections.

We're in a service industry, and we have customers sign off at the end of the project that all requirements are fulfilled. Can we use this as our release of product and services?

Yes, that would work. You're free to specify who performs release of services and how it's accomplished.

8.6 FREQUENTLY ASKED QUESTIONS

Our employees do a quick visual inspection of products before they're shipped. Do we need to keep records of this?

Yes. If this is a product verification you have deemed necessary, then records are required. Find a simple and transparent way of capturing the record.

8.7 CONTROL OF NONCONFORMING OUTPUTS

Equivalent to clause 8.3 in ISO 9001:2008.

Nonconforming outputs are goods or services that don't meet requirements. The requirements can come from a variety of sources, including internal requirements, customer requirements, and statutory or regulatory requirements. The purpose of controlling nonconforming outputs is to contain and minimize their effects. Control of nonconforming outputs is a close cousin to corrective action. Nonconforming outputs don't always result in formal corrective action, but it's always a consideration.

A system for controlling nonconformities is, by its very nature, defensive. Its purpose is to contain problems and prevent them from reaching and/or further affecting customers. Implementing a great system won't make an organization world class. On the other hand, a poor system can cause very serious problems and possibly even lead to the organization's demise. Therefore, it makes sense to construct an effective system that everyone will use and understand.

What is a nonconforming output?

It may be useful to define exactly what a nonconforming output is. For such an output to exist, one or more of the following conditions must be present:

- *Formal verification activities.* By definition, nonconforming outputs result from verification, inspection, or test activities. If these don't exist at a particular stage of product realization, then nonconforming outputs generally don't exist either. The exception is the case of nonconforming service, which is often identified through casual observation or customer feedback, as opposed to a formal inspection of any sort. Remember that when we say verification, inspection, or test activities, we're talking about "release of products and services" (clause 8.6) in the vernacular of ISO 9001:2015.

- *Removing a product from the material flow or production process.* If a product's condition allows it to be handled in the normal production flow, the organization may elect to handle the product outside its nonconforming product procedures. This only works if there are formal verification activities that take place downstream in the production process.

- *Operating conditions intended to produce conforming products.* If process conditions aren't intended to produce conforming products, the organization may handle the results of these processes outside its nonconforming product procedures. A service example might be a missed repair call because the business wasn't open. The customer who tried to schedule the repair might be irritated, but the business wasn't open at the time and the operating conditions weren't intended to produce products. A manufacturing example might be a production line that unavoidably produces a certain amount of start-up scrap. The scrap is simply part of getting the process up to normal operating conditions. The organization could elect to handle this product outside of its procedures for nonconforming products, especially when the scrap or waste in no way resembles conforming product. Trouble arises when the scrap or waste looks exactly like conforming product, as it does in many industries, such as chemical manufacturing. In these cases, potential misidentification outweighs other factors and makes nonconforming product procedures a necessity.

- *Risk to the organization.* Regardless of any other considerations, an organization can decide that the business risk or potential liability is great enough to treat outputs as nonconforming at any particular stage of the process. Regardless of ISO 9001 requirements, this is the category that matters most when deciding if something is nonconforming.

Even given these guidelines, an organization may discover a considerable amount of gray area regarding what is or isn't nonconforming outputs. This is only natural and a reflection of the real-life complexities of business. The organization must look objectively at its own operations, analyze its unique risk factors, and decide what will be included within its system for nonconforming outputs. Some situations will be quite obvious; others won't.

8.7 FREQUENTLY ASKED QUESTIONS

We manufacture a product that requires a number of adjustments and tweaks before it meets requirements. Do we have to consider the product nonconforming while we're working to bring it into specification?

No. The product isn't at a point where it's expected to meet requirements. Identify the formal verification points in your process. That's where control of nonconforming outputs will definitely apply.

We use customer feedback as a way to identify nonconforming service. We don't make and inspect a tangible product, so we feel this is one of the best ways to identify problems. Will this work?

Yes. Applying these requirements to a service organization will take some creativity, and this sounds like a perfectly reasonable way to do it. Keep in mind that your internal checks of service work might also identify nonconformities.

8.7.1 (No subclause title)

Identifying nonconforming outputs

The first requirement for nonconforming outputs in ISO 9001:2015 states that outputs which don't conform to product requirements are identified and controlled. The two key words here are "identification" and "control." Let's address identification first.

Simply put, an organization must identify products that don't conform to requirements. This is an extension of the requirement for identifying all products by suitable means throughout product realization. Everything must be identified. However, the standard doesn't prescribe any particular methods of identifying nonconforming products. Indeed, it can take many forms, all of which have their place:

- *Identification of nonconforming products:*
  - ✓ Tags, signs, or labels affixed to the product
  - ✓ Labeled bins, boxes, and bags
  - ✓ Remarks or descriptions written directly on the product
  - ✓ Tape or ribbon wrapped around the product
  - ✓ Paint spots or other coded markings on the product
  - ✓ Electronic identification, often by means of a barcode affixed to the product
  - ✓ Storing the product in specially marked areas

- *Identification of nonconforming services:*
  - ✓ Work order notated with problems that occurred during a service call
  - ✓ Note stapled to a customer receipt
  - ✓ Completion of a nonconforming service report
  - ✓ Chalkboard, grease board, or bulletin board with details about nonconforming services
  - ✓ Intranet page, database, or spreadsheet with details about nonconforming services

Identification of nonconforming products typically involves visible identifiers on or near the product. Identification of nonconforming services, on the other hand, usually involves records that are tied to a job or transaction.

The organization is responsible for deciding which forms of identification are most appropriate for its operations. No universal conventions exist for what nonconforming identification should look like. Is a green "rejected" tag OK? Sure, if that's what the organization wants to use. How about the words "service failure" scrawled in crayon on the work order? No problem.

The identification system needn't be conventional. What's important is that it's effective and understood by users.

Controlling nonconforming outputs

Control is the next issue ISO 9001:2015 requires organizations to address, and it encompasses a wide range of potential activities:

* Establishing special handling requirements
* Segregating goods from conforming products
* Securing goods in locked or protected areas
* Establishing documented procedures
* Defining responsibilities and authorities
* Training employees on procedures
* Defining timeframes for taking action
* Defining dispositions
* Recording nonconformities
* Connections to the corrective action system

In other words, "control" summarizes all the methods that lead to two desired outcomes: preventing nonconforming products from reaching and/or further affecting the customer, and eliminating the causes of nonconforming products. Identification is actually a component of control, although the standard treats it separately.

Nonconforming outputs detected after delivery or use

Occasionally—but hopefully not often—nonconformities will be detected after delivery or after the customer has used the product. The organization must take action appropriate to the effects or potential effects of the nonconformity. This can mean a number of things. Typically, with goods, organizations institute a returned goods process to deal with nonconformities that are detected after delivery or use.

For most goods, this system works fairly well and follows this general sequence:

1. The customer contacts the organization to report the nonconformity.

2. If it's determined to be appropriate, the customer is issued a tracking number of some sort. This number is often referred to as returned materials authorization (RMA) or returned goods authorization (RGA).

3. The customer is asked to mail or ship the product back to the organization, referencing the assigned tracking number.

4. When the product returns to the organization, it's handled much like any other nonconformity. The primary difference is that there may be the additional issue of crediting the customer for all or part of the product's cost.

5. Corrective action is initiated to determine and eliminate the root cause of the nonconformity, as with in any other nonconforming product situation. The key benefit of a returned goods process is that the organization can see the nonconformity for itself, rather than just hearing about it.

Sometimes the effects of the nonconformity may require more or less action than the returned goods process described above. For wide-ranging or potentially harmful nonconformities, the organization may institute a universal recall of all products sold within a certain time period. For very small nonconformities, the customer may simply receive an automatic credit and be asked to discard the nonconforming product. In any case, the organization must consider the nonconformity's effects and take action that logically matches those effects.

Some organizations stipulate time limits within which a disposition must be accomplished (e.g., "Nonconforming products must be dispositioned within 30 days of being identified"). However, common sense dictates that some dispositions may take longer to arrive at than others. Time limits are rarely a good idea, and they usually result in the organization violating its own procedures. If organizations want to reduce the amount of time between identification and disposition, managers simply need to monitor products in their nonconforming areas, although this responsibility is often ignored.

Should your process be documented (i.e., maintained in documented information)?

ISO 9001:2015 doesn't require you to maintain documented information of your process for nonconforming outputs. Should you anyway? In most cases, yes. This process is simply too important to leave to "tribal knowledge." Try to make your procedure simple and concise. How complex is your system for controlling nonconforming products? Probably not very. Ensure that the documented procedure is equally uncomplicated. The organization might consider using graphic explanations such as flow diagrams to make the procedure more intuitive and user-friendly.

Responsibilities and authorities should be defined clearly in the documented procedure for each stage of control. Consider the following issues within the procedure:

- Who can identify nonconforming goods or services?
- Who can move or handle nonconforming goods?
- What kind of communication should take place about nonconforming products?
- Who can authorize disposition of nonconforming goods or services?
- Who can perform the disposition?

These responsibilities and authorities should be addressed in a no-nonsense manner, and the persons who have responsibilities and authorities within the system should receive appropriate training. Defined responsibilities and authorities are useless if nobody knows about them.

Dealing with nonconforming outputs

ISO 9001:2015 next addresses "dealing" with nonconforming outputs. Previous versions of the standard referred to this as dispositioning nonconforming products. Dispositioning has a clear definition to most people in the quality assurance community. ISO 9001:2015 offers four possible ways to deal with nonconforming outputs:

- *Correction of the nonconformity.* The product will maintain its basic identity, but its nonconformity will be corrected. This can occur in a variety of ways:

✓ By re-performing the service and correctly providing the desired service, either in whole or in part.

✓ By repairing the product. This includes actions that make the product functional, although it doesn't conform perfectly to the original requirements. Such a product may not carry the same warranty as first-quality products.

✓ By reworking the product. Actions that make the product conform to the original requirements. In the customers' eyes, this product is exactly the same as a first-quality conforming product.

✓ By reprocessing the product and sending it back through the transformation process. This is done in many continuous process industries, such as chemicals and plastics.

- *Segregation, containment, return, or suspension.* This is a very broad category. Let's briefly discuss each one.

✓ Segregation isn't really a way to permanently "deal" with nonconformities. It's a way to control the nonconforming output from being used or distributed. Truly dealing with it would be what you do after the product has been segregated. At any rate, ISO 9001:2015 provides this as an option. Containment is basically the same thing as segregation, though it can be more clearly interpreted as applying to a service.

✓ Returning a nonconforming product is an option if it came from a supplier or other external provider. It's common for organizations to reject a product right on the shipping dock before it's even unloaded. In this regard, the product is returned before it's even formally received. In other cases, nonconforming products are discovered after receiving and even after use has begun. When this happens, an RGA or RMA is usually requested from the supplier. The product is then returned to the supplier referencing the RGA or RMA number provided by the supplier.

✓ Suspension simply means stopping something. This would generally apply to a service that—upon discovering a nonconforming condition—is stopped until deciding what to do next.

- *Informing the customer.* This sort of disposition is appropriate when the organization discovers that nonconforming product has been delivered or nonconforming service has been performed. Often this discovery takes place before the customer even realizes that he or she has received nonconforming outputs. It's a professional courtesy to notify customers as quickly as possible if they've received something from you that doesn't meet requirements. Simply coming to the conclusion that "we should wait and see if they notice" is a very bad policy when it comes to dealing with nonconformities. If the customer doesn't notice now, they will eventually.

- *Authorizing release by concession.* In this case, the product still doesn't meet requirements. Nothing has been done to eliminate the nonconformity or alter the good or service's quality. However, somebody has decided to use, release, or accept the product anyway. If a product is nonconforming according to the organization's internal specifications but acceptable according to the customer's specifications, a concession can be issued by the organization. However, if the product is nonconforming according to the customer's specifications, the concession can only come from the customer.

  The term "concession" may cause some confusion. It's nothing more than an agreement to use, release, or accept a product. Concessions are always recorded; otherwise, they're worthless. If no record of the concession exists, then the organization has nothing to defend itself with in the case of later disputes. Moreover, ISO 9001 requires concessions to be recorded. Concessions normally include the following details:

  ✓ The condition or quality level that has been accepted

  ✓ The identification of the good or service that is covered under the concession

  ✓ The person who has authorized the concession, including a signature, if possible

  ✓ The date and time the concession was granted

  These could be recorded on the original sales order, the customer's purchase order, internal quality assurance records, or other relevant documentation. Regardless of where and how the concession is recorded, the important thing is that it's clear and unambiguous.

Reverifying after correction

When nonconforming products are corrected, they must be reverified. This verification must match the original requirements that the product was intended to meet—otherwise, you've regraded the product. Reverification can be done through the original inspection process or by a completely different function—it doesn't matter. The important thing is that the reverification is recorded, just like any formal verification.

Two elements must be included in this record:

- Evidence of conformity with acceptance criteria (i.e., actual measurements or observations)
- Identification of the person authorizing the release (i.e., the person performing the verification or responsible for seeing that the task is performed)

The reverification record can be kept anywhere that makes sense to the organization. The only imperative is that the relevant people know where it is and can retrieve it.

8.7.2 (No subclause title)

Retained documented information (i.e., records)

ISO 9001:2015 requires you to retain documented information related to nonconforming outputs. The recordkeeping is relatively simple and has great value in data analysis and trending. The following items must be recorded:

- A description of the nonconformity
- Actions taken
- Details of concessions, if any
- Identification of who decided actions to be taken on the nonconformity

Because we've already discussed documenting the concession, let's focus on the other three items. The description of the nonconformity and action taken can easily be recorded on the form that identifies the product as non-conforming. Keep it simple. Like most paperwork, the more complex a record is, the fewer employees will use it. The best option is electronic record-keeping, particularly for organizations that identify nonconforming products through barcodes or other electronic means. The actions taken are what you actually did to the nonconformity with a focus on making sure it wasn't incorrectly used, processed, or delivered. Identification of who decided what actions to be taken on the nonconformity simply provides traceability and accountability.

Connection to corrective action

Do all instances of nonconforming outputs result in corrective action? This is a very good question, and the answer requires some interpretation. The organization must evaluate, among other considerations, the organizational risk and potential effect on customer satisfaction and then take appropriate action. As long as there's evidence that the organization has performed this evaluation and has an objective basis for its action—or nonaction—then nobody should object.

Keep in mind that the corrective action system is worthless if it's not used. An organization should look for every possible opportunity to use it and enforce causal investigation into nonconformities. Clearly, the link between corrective actions and control of nonconforming outputs is one of the most critical relationships within any management system. In the end, your system for controlling nonconforming outputs will be fatally flawed if it doesn't include a clear and direct connection to your corrective action system.

Chapter 7

ISO 9001:2015 Section 9 Performance Evaluation

9.1 MONITORING, MEASUREMENT, ANALYSIS, AND EVALUATION

9.1.1 General

Equivalent to clause 8.1 in ISO 9001:2008.

This section provides an introduction to performance evaluation. It addresses your approach for monitoring and measurement, followed by a strategy for analysis and evaluation. Some of this is review. We've already discussed ISO 9001:2015's requirement for monitoring of quality objectives (6.2), as well as the requirements for monitoring and measurement of quality management system (QMS) processes (4.4.1(c)). We've also talked about release of products and services, which of course involves monitoring and measuring them (8.6). Section 9 pulls all of these requirements together. We're also validating that we're doing the right thing with regard to performance evaluation. Have you already addressed the performance evaluation through meeting the other requirements? Possibly, but we're going to double check now. Let's take a look at each of the bulleted requirements of this section.

- *Determine what needs to be monitored and measured.* This could constitute dozens or even hundreds of different things. The purpose is to make sure we haven't forgotten anything important. ISO 9001:2015 requires monitoring and measurement of the following:
  - ✓ Information about external and internal issues/the organization's context (4.1)
  - ✓ Information about interested parties and their requirements (4.2)
  - ✓ QMS processes (4.4)
  - ✓ Quality objectives (6.2.1(e))
  - ✓ Conformity of products and services (7.1.5.1)
  - ✓ Performance of external providers (8.4.1)
  - ✓ Ensuring that externally provided products meet requirements (8.4.2(d))
  - ✓ Customer perceptions (9.1.2)
  - ✓ Analyze and evaluate appropriate data and information arising from monitoring and measurement (9.1.3). Clause 9.3 provides a consolidated list of items you must evaluate.

- *Methods for monitoring, measurement, analysis, and evaluation.* A method provides guidance for action. That's exactly what you're being asked to do. Your QMS should include methods that answer the following questions:
  - ✓ *What will be monitored, measured, analyzed, and evaluated?* Some of these items are listed above, but many more will come from a deeper exploration of the standard and from your internal needs.
  - ✓ *Where will the monitoring, measurement, analysis, and evaluation take place?* Which meetings or processes will perform these tasks?
  - ✓ *Who will be involved?* Few things happen without clear responsibilities and authorities.

- *When will the monitoring and measurement be performed?* The frequency of an activity is one of its most important details from a control standpoint. Clearly state the frequency and timing of monitoring and measurement and provide oversight to ensure it happens. Your internal audit process will be one of the key oversight functions.

- *When will results be analyzed and evaluated?* There are always two steps to an effective process for performance evaluation: monitoring and measuring what matters to our success, and analyzing and evaluating the monitoring results so we can understand their meaning. If the analysis and evaluation takes place separately from the monitoring and measurement, determine when they will happen.

- *Evaluate the performance and effectiveness of the QMS.* All the monitoring, measurement, analysis, and evaluation that you're in the process of defining will ultimately shed light on the performance and effectiveness of the QMS. Three items in particular will be especially helpful in illustrating how effective your QMS is:

  ✓ *Quality objectives.* These are the strategic measures that tell you whether your QMS efforts are bearing any fruit.

  ✓ *Internal audits.* This process is specifically designed to evaluate the intent, implementation, and effectiveness of the QMS.

  ✓ *Management review.* One of top management's most important tools, it reveals the organization's progress and how the QMS is facilitating long-term success.

- *Retain documented information (i.e., records).* The final sentence of subclause 9.1.1 highlights its importance. This means that you will keep records of monitoring, measurement, analysis, and evaluation unless there is a very good reason not to. In most cases, you'll simply keep records. Please note that it makes sense to implement subclauses 9.1.1 and 9.1.3 together. The two topics are too similar to be treated as different entities.

9.1.2 Customer satisfaction

Equivalent to subclause 8.2.1 of ISO 9001:2008.

This is a very short part of ISO 9001:2015, but it's one of its most powerful. If implemented correctly, the customer satisfaction requirements will deliver lasting value and customer loyalty to the organization. The specific requirements of ISO 9001:2015 remain nearly identical to the previous requirements, with the following subtle differences:

- Customer expectations were added. Previous versions of ISO 9001 required the organization to monitor customer perceptions of meeting requirements. Now you must monitor perceptions of meeting needs and expectations. Is this a big difference? No. In the mind of most customers, needs and expectations flow together on a sliding continuum.
- Methods for monitoring and reviewing customer perceptions were added. In the past, organizations had to determine methods for using customer perceptions. Again, not much of a difference.

This subclause is only two sentences long, which leaves room for a lot of interpretation. Let's provide some guidance on what you need to do to meet these requirements and provide value.

Monitor customers' perceptions

The key word in this requirement is "perceptions." A perception originates from someone's mind. It doesn't necessarily have any connection to facts or data. Perceptions are simply beliefs. Customer perceptions are especially important because customers act on the things they believe, and these actions affect your organization. Even if the belief stems from a perception that was factually incorrect, the resulting action will be a fact.

Perceptions are very broad, and certainly include both positive and negative opinions. This is why your process for capturing customer perceptions should have the ability to capture both types of feedback. Simply having a complaint process doesn't enable you to capture positive feedback. The best processes for capturing feedback use a mix of proactive and reactive methods, though the real value is in proactive methods.

Degree to which needs and expectations have been fulfilled

You're being asked to monitor two potentially different values:
- The degree to which customer needs are fulfilled
- The degree to which customer expectations are fulfilled

Technically, they are two different issues. Customer needs (i.e., requirements) are defined as part of the order, contract, schedule, or statement of work. In other words, they're formally stated and agreed to by both parties.

This differs from an expectation, which only originates from one of the parties and may not even be formally stated. It could reside in somebody's mind, only peeking out at odd and inconvenient moments. Although only a formally stated need is enforceable from a legal standpoint, you should be just as concerned with expectations. Why? Because customers act like needs and expectations are the same thing. It's the same paradigm as facts and perceptions being the same thing. Make sure that your customer feedback methods specifically probe expectations. If you use an open-ended feedback tool, expectations will automatically be added, because that's the way customers think.

Determine methods for collecting and using feedback

ISO 9001:2015 requires that you define your methods for capturing customer perceptions. In a practical sense, this simply means that you establish the method. If the method is complex or shared by many people, then "determine" should be interpreted as "document." Whether to document your procedure is your choice. The tool you use to capture feedback will most likely be a document of some sort.

The other half of the requirement defines how you will use the customer perceptions. This is even more important than the gathering of perceptions. Many organizations do a good job of getting customer feedback; far fewer are good at doing something about it. You have some built-in processes for monitoring and reviewing data and information within your ISO 9001-compliant QMS. The foremost is management review, discussed in clause 9.3. Management review is top management's formal review of the system and other relevant inputs and its subsequent decisions based on the data. An argument can be made for analyzing customer feedback in some place other than management review, as top management usually has too many other things to consider during that forum. Customer feedback is a very strategic type of information, and top management should analyze it. Here are a few of the places that customer feedback could be used and acted upon:

- Management review
- Business planning meetings
- Design team meetings
- Marketing group meetings

- Quality assurance meetings
- Companywide events

In many organizations, customer feedback analysis and action is the responsibility of the quality assurance team. This happens almost by default, because nobody else feels like dealing with it. Quality assurance is certainly equipped to analyze trends and take action. Customer feedback represents a huge opportunity to engage the rest of the organization in customer satisfaction. Don't make customer feedback understood only by a cabal within the organization. There's nothing more important to the organization's success than customer feedback, so make it a frequent communication topic at all levels of the organization.

When action is taken on customer feedback, make sure to use your corrective action process. ISO 9001:2015 doesn't require this, but it accomplishes a number of purposes:

- Tracking of actions to completion
- Clear assignment of responsibility
- Automatic scrutiny by management review
- Visibility to other parts of the organization

The bottom line is that customer feedback without some kind of action is worthless. Take action on the biggest opportunities and risks revealed by customer feedback and follow through on your initiatives.

Because ISO 9001:2015 leaves a lot of discretion to the organization, let's discuss the topic of customer satisfaction in more detail.

Why traditional customer surveys are a bad idea

Scaled customer surveys are among the most widely used tools in business. Unfortunately, they're also some of the worst. There's nothing bad about surveys, but they can turn an inherently simple task—such as gathering customer feedback—into something complex and unwieldy. When that happens there's a good chance it won't satisfy its original purpose, which in this case is making improvements. Why exactly are surveys the wrong tool for most organizations? Let's explore the reasons and then consider an alternative approach that's far more appropriate.

- *Surveys don't produce timely data.* Most traditional customer surveys are sent out periodically to a sampling of an organization's customers, typically once or twice a year. This is a manageable frequency from an administrative standpoint because implementing a survey requires a significant dedication of time and effort. The downside is that by the time the organization receives the feedback, the information is at least six months old. The information is almost worthless because customers have already acted on their perceptions before the organization has a chance to respond. Customers don't wait around to tell you what they're going to do before they do it. If you're not regularly tuned into your customers, you'll never know what hit you.

  It makes more sense to gather customer feedback continually. Make the customer feedback process a continual process, not a grand event that occurs once or twice a year. This consumes far fewer resources and it also ensures that the information is current. If you can't take action on customer perceptions quickly, you lose your opportunity.

- *Too many questions.* Another downfall of most surveys is that they try to do too much. They probe the customer experience from every imaginable angle. Although admirable, this approach results in long, unwieldy surveys that most customers run away from as fast as they can. I have gotten into the habit of scrawling "TOO LONG" in huge block letters on these kinds of surveys. I'm providing feedback, but not exactly the kind expected. Most people don't even bother to provide this much; they simply toss long surveys into the trash.

  The key to successful customer feedback is to ask about the few aspects of the customer experience that matter the most. By asking about everything under the sun, you're establishing the expectation that you'll take action on everything, which is impossible. You're also telling your customer, "Your time isn't very valuable, so the imposition of this long and boring survey should be no problem for you." Focus on a few vital issues, and these obstacles go away. The dilemma is that most organizations don't know what the few vital issues are, thus the need for long surveys. Your organization must know what really matters to its customers.

- *Difficult to design.* If you like defusing explosives, you'll love creating surveys. They include so many failure modes that they're nearly impossible to design correctly unless you do it for a living. Why are they so hard? Let's examine two of their more challenging aspects: questions and scales.

Most surveys comprise a series of questions or statements, followed by a response scale. The response scale usually represents degrees of satisfaction (e.g., "very satisfied," "satisfied," "neutral," etc.) or degrees of agreement (e.g., "strongly agree," "agree," "neutral," etc.). Both of these scales present huge challenges. Most people don't have the writing skills to craft clear, unambiguous survey questions. The result is that the questions don't accurately reflect the attribute that's being queried. In the spirit of getting the job done, customers will often take a guess at what the questions really mean. Like all guessing games, sometimes they'll be right and other times wrong. At best, your data will be 50 percent valid—not very good odds.

In the unlikely event that the survey questions are clear, there's still the obstacle of designing a logical response scale. This would seem to be an easy task, but it's extremely complex. Typical errors I've observed are scales that aren't balanced, scales that are biased, scales that don't have equal intervals between the points, scales that don't match the question or statement, and scales that have too many degrees of resolution. If the scale is flawed, then the data that come from it are also flawed. "Garbage in, garbage out," as the saying goes.

- *No direction for improvement.* The fourth downfall of traditional surveys is that they don't provide much guidance for improvement. Sure, they provide data, but what actions are you going to take based on the data? For example, let's imagine that you've asked customers to rate the technical knowledge of your sales force. The average response is 3.4 on a five-point scale, roughly halfway between "neither good nor bad" and "good." What does this number really mean? Even more important, what are you going to do about it? The data help you produce fancy charts, but they probably won't steer you toward specific improvements.

If you aren't able to take action on survey data, their value as improvement tools is zero. Had you asked customers an open-ended question such as, "What do you think is our biggest customer-service weakness?" you might have received some feedback that provided a clear path for improvement. In the world of customer perception, data don't always rule. By their nature, perceptions are qualitative and subjective. Attempts to produce data from such a fuzzy source can be misleading. It's better to get actionable information than to attempt to turn human beings into precise measuring instruments. If you capture customer perceptions, analyze the trends, and take action, you've accomplished a lot.

So, what should you do to capture customer perceptions? I recommend a five-step process:

1. *Examine your existing customer interactions.* Your interactions with your customers are limitless. These contacts are conducted via telephone, e-mail, mail, fax, and in person. Because you already have numerous contacts with your customers, there's no reason to invent a new contact for the sake of collecting customer feedback. Use the connections you already have and all parties will generally be much happier.

2. *Choose an interaction suited to collecting feedback.* Not all customer contacts are created equally. In general, the contact should be neutral, routine, and candid. Here's what each of these mean:

    ✓ *Neutral.* Neutral contact isn't related to an existing problem or complaint. Attempting to collect feedback when a customer already has a problem is obnoxious and counterproductive. Use an interaction that's neutral in tone and purpose, such as a query or order placement.

    ✓ *Routine.* This contact happens regularly. Feedback collected from routine interactions of this sort is likely to be fresher.

    ✓ *Candid.* This contact occurs between parties that trust one another and are willing to communicate freely. A candid relationship is key to collecting accurate and representative perceptions.

3. *Develop a tool that's matched to the customer interaction.* Choosing the right tool for the job is critical in every endeavor, and that goes for collecting feedback, too. Once the organization has selected an appropriate customer interaction for collecting feedback, it must develop a tool that works in that context. This is a subjective task and certain guidelines can assist in knowing what tools work best in different situations, such as:

✓ *Telephone contact.* An unobtrusive tool that's conducted at the end of a routine telephone call. Brevity is critical with this kind of tool because most people are anxious to get off the phone once their business is completed.

✓ *In-person visit.* A tool that enables the company to see its product in use, just as the customer experiences the product or service. The tool should also enable different people to be queried, depending on the nature of the feedback sought.

✓ *After service or consumption.* A tool that enables the customer to conveniently provide "flash feedback." Make the return of this feedback seamless. If the customer has to expend any effort to return the feedback, it probably won't be returned.

✓ *Email.* A live link within the body of the message that takes customers to a simple and visually appealing evaluation of their experience. Make sure the link works fast and is compatible with a variety of Internet browsers and computer monitors.

✓ *Benchmark customer feedback tools with other organizations.* There's no virtue in being original. Borrow good ideas and approaches as you see them. Hundreds, if not thousands, of examples exist for each of the tools described above. See what other people are doing and adapt the methods to your own needs.

4. *Focus on open-ended questions.* If you want to grab the attention of your customers, ask them what they like and don't like. It's that simple. Asking simple, open-ended questions of this sort enables customers to dictate the content of their feedback. You'll hear what's important to them. This is exactly the sort of feedback you want. Trends in open-ended feedback will keep you informed on the issues that customers care most about, something that many organizations don't understand.

Open-ended feedback also provides a clear path to improvement. Numerical ratings can help you prioritize issues, but they don't tell you exactly what to do. Open-ended feedback can. When 75 percent of your customers answer the question, "What makes you most frustrated about being our customer?" in the same way, you know exactly what you need to do to improve. There's no ambiguity.

Open-ended feedback doesn't help you make fancy charts. But do you really need more fancy charts to cover the walls of the conference room? No, you need improved customer satisfaction and loyalty. Open-ended feedback will reveal exactly what actions lead to long-term success, which is much more important than fancy charts. Here are my favorite open-ended questions. Three are about all you need.

✓ *Do you have any problems with our products that you haven't told us about?*

✓ *Is there anything you think we do particularly well?*

✓ *What could we do in the future that would make your job easier?*

5. *Act on your opportunities.* Action is the most critical step of the entire process. It starts with identifying trouble areas. Problems revealed through feedback must be addressed immediately. This is the business equivalent of triage: Stop the bleeding and stabilize the patient. Let's hope you won't discover too many issues that require triage, but it's better to learn of these proactively while the customer is still your customer, and not a former customer.

After addressing the trouble areas, the organization must analyze the trends. Open-ended feedback follows the same rules as most traditional numerical data: It tends to clump into categories. Group the feedback into categories and apply Pareto analysis to the results. Your opportunity areas will quickly emerge. Input these opportunities into your corrective action system and track them to completion. Treat every improvement action as a mini project, with assigned tasks, responsibilities, time frames, resources, and reviews. The more sunlight shines on your improvement action, the better it will be. In other words, communicate widely. The final communication about your improvement will be to your customer: "Here's what we've done based on your feedback." These may be the most important words you ever say—and you don't have to use a traditional customer survey to say them.

9.1.2 FREQUENTLY ASKED QUESTIONS

Can we use our complaint program to satisfy the customer satisfaction requirements?

You can use it, but it can't be your only method of capturing customer feedback. Since ISO 9001:2015 requires you to monitor customer perceptions, there must be a proactive aspect to your feedback to ensure the full range of possible perceptions. There's nothing proactive about waiting for customers to complain.

Do we have to capture feedback from internal customers?

The intent of this requirement is to capture the feedback of customers outside the scope of your management system. This could be another branch of your company or a different firm altogether. You don't have to capture customer feedback between departments within your organization unless you see value in it.

9.1.3 Analysis and evaluation

Equivalent to clause 8.4 in ISO 9001:2008.

This section is related to subclause 9.1.1. They go together like a hand and glove. In fact, you can't implement one without the other. While subclause 9.1.1 is concerned primarily with monitoring and measurement, this section is primarily concerned with analysis and evaluation. Let's take a brief look at the sources of data that are required to be analyzed and evaluated:

- *Conformity of products and services.* You're looking for inspection trends. How many of our products fail, and why? How often does a service not meet customer requirements and what causes it? Your objective is to figure out how to make your product or service better. As with all data, trends and graphical depictions facilitate interpretations. Here are some useful categories of product conformity data:
  - ✓ In-process inspection rates
  - ✓ Final inspection rates

✓ Types of product defects
✓ Products with the highest and lowest rates of nonconformity
✓ Trends in return and warranty rates
✓ Test data
✓ Product audit results
✓ Process capability against specifications
✓ Performance against project plan
✓ On-time delivery rate
✓ Service effectiveness
✓ Jobs completed according to schedule

- *Customer satisfaction.* What exactly are our customers telling us? What do they like? What do they not like? What seems to be the "deal break-ers" in their minds? Strive for specifics and carefully examine the data for trends. Consolidating data into categories will help create graphical representations (charts, graphs, and diagrams) that are easier to interpret. And remember that analysis without action is worthless, especially when it comes to customer feedback. Collect it, analyze it, and take action to improve it. Here are some particularly useful types of customer satisfac-tion data:
  ✓ Biggest complaints categories
  ✓ Most frequently desired features
  ✓ Positive comments and praise
  ✓ Most important product attributes
  ✓ Biggest product strengths
  ✓ Complaints per million dollars in sales
  ✓ Specific ideas and suggestions
  ✓ Response rates from customer feedback tools
  ✓ Improvements to the process for capturing feedback

- *Effectiveness of the QMS.* There are many measures and indicators that could be used for this. The most obvious is internal audit results. The en-tire focus of an internal audit is on the intent, implementation, and effec-tiveness of the QMS. Quantitative data tied to internal audits often has unintended effects in terms of the behavior it motivates (e.g., tracking the number of audit nonconformities, which just ends up discouraging accurate audits). A better analysis would be the effectiveness of corrective action that result from nonconformities.

- *Effectiveness of planning.* ISO 9001:2015 includes far more planning and strategizing than previous iterations. More is not necessarily better, though. The planning requirements basically fall into three categories:
  - ✓ Actions to address risks and opportunities (6.1)
  - ✓ Planning to achieve quality objectives (6.2.2)
  - ✓ Planning of changes (6.3)

  Analysis of these items will indicate how well the organization has planned based on its ability to mitigate risks, achieve objectives, and implement changes in the organization.

- *Action on risks and opportunities.* This is really a repeat of the previous requirement related to planning. Clearly, risks and opportunities are a kind of planning, so these categories overlap one another.

- *Performance of suppliers and subcontractors.* Your success is tied to the success of your suppliers and subcontractors. You're already evaluating their performance as part of addressing clause 8.4. If you establish meaningful criteria for evaluating external providers, this requirement will be easy to satisfy. Here are some typical types of supplier data:
  - ✓ Trends in pricing
  - ✓ On-time performance
  - ✓ Conformity of products
  - ✓ Responsiveness to inquiries and requests
  - ✓ Corrective actions taken by suppliers
  - ✓ Supplier audit performance
  - ✓ Supplier solvency and viability
  - ✓ Knowledge of supplier personnel
  - ✓ Candidates for supplier awards

- *Need for improvements to the QMS.* This category is a culmination of all the previous data and information sources. You consider all the various data trends and information and decide what (if anything) should be done differently. This particular data source includes a wide range of additional issues that you could consider. Here are a number of items that will reflect on the need for QMS improvement:

✓ Trends of nonconformities during internal audits
✓ Employee suggestions
✓ Inability to successfully address risks
✓ Inability to achieve objectives
✓ Customer complaints in the same category or from the same cause
✓ Competitive analysis
✓ Findings revealed during investigation into the organization and its context
✓ Feedback from interested parties
✓ Change management plans that went awry
✓ Gaps in organizational knowledge
✓ Failures of external providers

As with any data source that's a culmination of other sources, there will be duplication and redundancy. This category doesn't have to be a unique source of data. The intent is that you reflect on how data and information sheds light on areas to improve your QMS. One of the unspoken themes of ISO 9001:2015 is that the QMS isn't just about quality anymore. It's about managing your organization for success.

If subclause 9.1.3 is the brother of subclause 9.1.1, then it also has to be the son of clause 9.3, Management review. What is the natural forum for analyzing and evaluating data? Management review, of course. It's no coincidence that the data and information sources you're being asked to analyze are almost identical to management review inputs. You could certainly analyze and evaluate data in other places and at other times, but management review is just screaming to be used for this purpose. The diagram shown in figure 7.1 illustrates the relationship between the three sections of ISO 9001:2015 we're discussing.

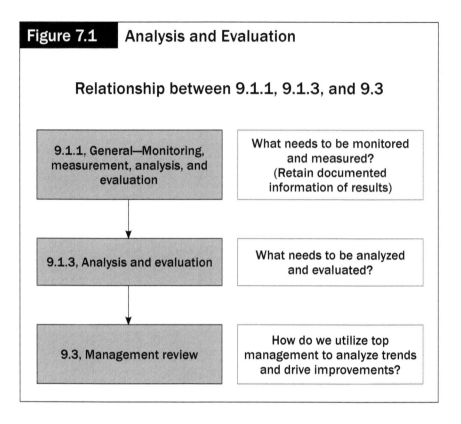

Figure 7.1   Analysis and Evaluation

Relationship between 9.1.1, 9.1.3, and 9.3

9.1.1, General—Monitoring, measurement, analysis, and evaluation	What needs to be monitored and measured? (Retain documented information of results)
9.1.3, Analysis and evaluation	What needs to be analyzed and evaluated?
9.3, Management review	How do we utilize top management to analyze trends and drive improvements?

9.1.3 FREQUENTLY ASKED QUESTIONS

All the items that must be analyzed and evaluated are already part of our management review. Do we have to invent new ways of analyzing this information?

No. ISO 9001:2015 doesn't specify how or where the analysis and evaluation will take place. Management review sounds like an especially good way to get the job done.

9.2 INTERNAL AUDITS

Equivalent to subclause 8.2.2 in ISO 9001:2008.

Internal auditing is one of the most important processes for driving improvement. During an internal audit, an organization's employees (or personnel acting on its behalf) look for evidence that it's met all relevant requirements of ISO 9001:2015 within its scope. It's inevitable that auditors will find where the organization hasn't met requirements. Nonconformities revealed by internal audits are treated as system issues (as opposed to personnel issues), and the organization takes corrective action to ensure that the system and related process prevent the problem from happening in the future. This isn't to say that nonconformities never result from personal negligence. They do. Smart organizations strive to fix their processes so that mistakes and errors happen less often. Let's examine the specific ISO 9001:2015 requirements of internal auditing.

Conduct internal audits at planned intervals

Audits are never a surprise. They are planned in advance, with personnel knowing exactly what processes will be covered and what requirements will apply. There are two general tools for planning audits:

- *Audit schedule.* The audit schedule shows the audits that will take place over an extended timeframe, typically six months or a year. It's available to all applicable personnel and subject to revision as circumstances change. We'll talk more about the types of issues that could trigger a change in the audit schedule later.

- *Audit plan.* This is a document that describes a single audit. It covers information such as the date and times of the audit; the audit scope, criteria, and objectives; who the auditors are; what areas will be covered and when; and anything else that will clarify the activity. The audit plan is provided to the auditees in advance of the audit, and it serves as a roadmap for what takes place. Like the schedule, it's subject to revision.

ISO 9001:2015 doesn't dictate how often you must conduct audits. The universal interpretation by certification bodies—which is almost always in their contract for registration services—is that you will audit all processes within the scope of your management system at least once a year. When you audit an internal process, you'll address whatever ISO 9001:2015 requirements are applicable, in addition to verifying internal procedures and policies. If an element of the standard doesn't apply to that particular department, you won't audit it in that area. Part of the audit planning process is gaining an understanding of what ISO 9001:2015 elements apply to what departments of your organization.

Determine whether the system conforms to the organization's own requirements

This is possibly the most meaningful source of audit requirements. Why? Because they're your requirements. They were developed specifically to meet the needs of your processes and products. These are the policies, procedures, work instructions, checklists, standard operating procedures, product specifications, and other issues you've committed yourself to within the scope of ISO 9001. As internal auditors, your personnel are especially well equipped to audit internal procedures because they observe them first hand. Part of the planning for an audit will be to determine which internal procedures, policies, and instructions relate to the audit in question. These are provided to auditors in advance to aid in their planning.

Determine whether the system conforms to ISO 9001:2015

You must also verify that your system and activities conform to ISO 9001:2015 requirements. This is often challenging for internal auditors because it's not always clear what the standard requires. That's why this book, or some other plain-spoken reference, should be standard reading for all internal auditors. However they arrive at it, all internal auditors need to understand how the requirements of ISO 9001:2015 relate to their own operations. This typically happens during auditor training and is reinforced by experience in applying the standard.

Determine whether the system is effectively implemented and maintained

This brings up the issue of effectiveness. You can meet all the requirements of ISO 9001:2015 and implement your own procedures but still not achieve effective results. The quickest way to know if a system is effective is through the exploration of three angles:

- Achievement of objectives
- Customer satisfaction
- Continual improvement

If there's evidence indicating these outcomes, then the system can usually be said to be effective.

Plan, establish, implement, and maintain an audit program

ISO 9001:2015 doesn't explicitly require that you maintain documented information (i.e., a procedure) on your internal audit program. It does give you a long list of items that you must plan, establish, implement, and maintain. Does a written procedure sound like a good idea? Of course. The decision is yours, but if we agree that auditing is one of the key drivers of improvement, it deserves to have a procedure guiding it. As concisely and simply as possible, say how you plan, conduct, report, and record audits. Make sure to include who performs these activities. Your internal audit procedure will be the guidebook for how audits are conducted, so it needs to be very clear. If you require the use of certain tools in your audits, they should be stipulated in your procedure. Here is a summary of the issues that are typically addressed in an internal audit procedure:

- Who maintains the audit schedule
- Training requirements for internal auditors
- How audits are planned and who conducts the planning
- Communication of the audit plan
- How evidence is gathered
- Guidelines for what constitutes a nonconformity
- How audit results are recorded

- Formal reporting requirements
- Corrective action on audit nonconformities
- Follow-up on corrective action to ensure effectiveness
- Review of audit results in management review

Consider importance of the processes, changes affecting the organization, and results of previous audits

ISO 9001:2015 states that the audit program shall consider these variables, but what it's really referring to is the audit schedule. The intent is that the audit schedule not be static. You will revise your audit schedule based on three general considerations:

- *Importance of the processes.* This means that parts of your organization that have higher importance will be audited more often. Why? Because they have a bigger effect on your success. If these processes fail, the organization will be seriously affected. You audit them to drive improvement where it matters the most and to prevent problems. What are some of the more important processes? This varies from one organization to the next, but these are almost universal:
  - ✓ Management review
  - ✓ Corrective action
  - ✓ Internal auditing
  - ✓ Actions to address risks and opportunities
  - ✓ Operational planning and control
  - ✓ Quality objectives

- *Changes affecting the organization.* Changes that you face will certainly influence what needs to be examined. For example, if the organization has a lot of employee turnover, the audit schedule might be expected to indicate more frequent audits in the areas of competence (7.2) and awareness (7.3). If the organization lost a major customer, then the schedule might show more audits in customer satisfaction (9.1.2). Change and planning for change are themes of ISO 9001:2015, and they certainly influence the audit program.

- *Results of previous audits.* How well or poorly a process performs in an audit will influence how often it's audited in the future. Do you know the reward for performing poorly during an audit? It's getting audited more frequently. The point is not to punish the process, but to aid in its improvement. Direct your audit resources where they're needed the most.

Audit criteria and scope for each audit

The audit criteria are what you're auditing against. Typical audit criteria are "ISO 9001:2015, the documented management system, and applicable customer requirements." The audit's scope is the departments, functions, and processes of your organization that are being audited. It's the boundaries of the audit. A typical audit scope is "Quoting, order taking, and scheduling functions at the Atlanta Regional Office." The audit criteria and scope are usually defined on the audit plan.

Objectivity and impartiality

When you schedule and plan audits, you will strive for objectivity and impartiality. That means not assigning auditors to audit areas in which they won't be able to clearly evaluate evidence. What could possibly cause prejudice during an audit? Here are some typical causes:
- Bad relations between the auditor and auditee
- Deep friendships between the auditor and auditee
- Auditor auditing the department in which he or she works

The trick to maintaining objectivity and impartiality is having enough internal auditors. Train a team of auditors every 12 to 18 months and continually build your "alumni association" of auditors. Over time, you'll have a large group of past and present internal auditors to choose from, and objectivity and impartiality will never be an issue.

Report results to management

One of the most important communications that take place within the QMS is the communication of audit results. The scope of the audit will dictate who within management will receive this message. The results are delivered verbally and visually during a closing meeting and in writing through an audit report. The results are typically communicated informally during the course of the audit to applicable managers. Communication is the blood that flows through the body of the audit.

Take correction and corrective action

This is where ISO 9001:2015 switches gears and starts talking about what you'll do with audit nonconformities. It's a simple equation: audit nonconformity equals corrective action. You don't pick and choose which audit nonconformities require corrective action. They all require corrective action. If your corrective action process makes this unwieldy or difficult, it's a good idea to revisit your corrective action procedure. I've heard interpretations of this requirement stating that simple correction may be adequate in some cases. I don't buy it. The actual requirement reads "take appropriate correction and corrective actions without undue delay." The word "and" indicates that both correction and corrective action are required. It's not an either-or proposition.

The statement "without undue delay" is quite vague. In general, this simply means that corrective action will be started within a reasonable interval of the audit. It seems reasonable that corrective action could begin within a week of the audit. How long it takes to finish corrective action depends on the complexity of the issue being addressed. Some audit nonconformities can be closed within a few days and others may take months. As long as your corrective action process shows steady progress on the issues and regular reporting, there's really no time limit for how long a corrective action can be open. The important thing is to take lasting and effective corrective action, not fast action. However, issues that affect employee health and safety often require lasting, effective, and fast corrective action.

Retain documented information of the audit program and results

Records demonstrate a number of things: audit planning, who was involved, evidence, positives and negatives revealed by the audit, and resulting corrective actions. ISO 9001:2015 simply states that you'll retain documented information (i.e., keep records) of audits and their results, which leaves the specifics up to you.

Here are the typical records related to an internal audit process:

- *Corrective actions.* These clearly show the nonconformities resulting from the audit. They also indicate cause(s), actions taken to address cause(s), and follow-up.
- *Audit notes and/or checklists.* These indicate proof of the audit having taken place and provide a record of the evidence collected. If the organization maintains records of audit plans and the respective audit reports, then audit notes/checklists wouldn't be required; the audit plans and audits reports together would provide adequate proof of the audit's occurrence.
- *Records of auditor training clearly showing that the auditors have met competency requirements set by the organization.* These records can be maintained where other training records are maintained. As mentioned earlier, it's typical for the audit procedure to specify what training is necessary for acting as an internal auditor.

Although the following records aren't required, you should strongly consider maintaining them:

- *Audit reports.* Many people are surprised to learn that ISO 9001 doesn't require audit reports. The standard simply requires that records be maintained of audit results. Audit reports are a recommended record because they provide a balanced of view of the entire audit. They also enable a strategic summary of the audit results, which is helpful for top management to digest the results at a glance.
- *Audit plans.* An audit plan details the hour-by-hour agenda for an individual audit. It guides the performance of the audit by telling who will do what and when.

What about audit follow-up?

ISO 9001:2015 doesn't address audit follow-up but it's strongly recommended. What are you following up on? The actions that were taken after the audit and whether they actually achieved anything. Some people consider this to be part of corrective action, but many organizations use their internal audit functions to verify these details. One way or another, the final step in the audit process is verifying that management took action on the audit nonconformities. Here's what someone would typically look for when verifying action on audit nonconformities:

- Do the actions taken relate to the identified causes?
- Have all actions been completed?
- Have all relevant documents been revised or written?
- If training was part of the corrective action, was it completed?
- Is there evidence that the causes of the nonconformity have been removed or reduced to an acceptable level?

As part of follow-up, you will record the results of actions taken. In other words, what was achieved with this corrective action? Be as clear as possible about what was determined. If a corrective action appears ineffective or incomplete, it should be resubmitted to management for more investigation and action.

Finally, keep in mind that audit results are an input to management review, as are corrective actions. The more graphic and strategic you can portray your audit results, the more they will capture the attention of top management.

9.2 FREQUENTLY ASKED QUESTIONS

Are we required to classify our internal audit nonconformities as major or minor, like certification bodies do?

No. Treating all audit nonconformities as being equally important can remove a lot of controversy and confusion from the audit process.

Do we have to use checklists during our internal audit?

No. There's nothing in ISO 9001:2015 that requires checklists for internal audits. Checklists could provide evidence that audits took place, though. They could also help guide the activities of less-experienced auditors.

9.2 FREQUENTLY ASKED QUESTIONS

Do we have to audit our internal audit process?

Yes, you're required to audit all aspects of your management system, including your internal audit process.

9.3 MANAGEMENT REVIEW

Equivalent to clause 5.6 in ISO 9001:2008, with additional requirements related to inputs.

Management review is one of the most important components of a management system. It's the process by which top management reviews the effectiveness of the system and analyzes the performance of the organization. ISO 9001:2015 doesn't include any guidance for how often this process should take place, but common sense dictates that it should happen regularly. Smart organizations align their management reviews with the regular cycle of reviewing organizational performance, which usually takes place on a monthly basis. However, the frequency is up to the organization.

Adding a meeting called ISO 9001 management review when there is already an existing performance review of the organization is nearly always a bad idea. For starters, no one needs another meeting to attend. Second, if it comes down to a choice between management review and the existing performance meeting, which one is going to prevail? The existing meeting will win, of course. Incorporate your management review into any existing performance review forums. You may have to add a topic or two to the agenda, but this is a much better option than establishing a completely new meeting for the purpose of meeting ISO 9001:2015 requirements.

It's also worth noting that nothing in ISO 9001:2015 says that management review will be a physical meeting. The standard requires that top management take part, but beyond this key stakeholder, it's up to the organization to decide who else to involve. Typically, organizations include their key decision makers as part of management review. No matter how the organization configures its management review, it must retain documented information (i.e., records).

The ultimate purpose of management review is to help the organization improve. Management review does this by analyzing information, making decisions, and taking the appropriate actions. It's not a passive process. If management review doesn't produce actions or decisions, it's failing in its duty to drive improvements.

Management review inputs

ISO 9001:2015 requires specific inputs to management review. The inputs are data and information that reveal organizational and management system effectiveness. These inputs include:

- *Status of action items.* Anyone who has ever attended a meeting knows that it can be difficult to know what was decided. Even when it's clear, it's almost always difficult to complete the agreed-upon action items. This input ties the management reviews together and ensures that action items don't get forgotten.

- *Changes in the organization's context.* Do you remember this requirement? Way back in clause 4.1 of ISO 9001:2015 we talked about "Understanding the organization and its context," which determined external and internal issues that bear on the organization's success. Management studies this research during management review. Has anything changed? These could include changes related to economics, demographics, competition, suppliers, products, processes, laws, or anything else that affects the organization. Have our strengths or weaknesses shifted? Have new opportunities or threats been detected? These are the issues you're discussing during management review.

- *Customer satisfaction.* Customer feedback is the most important communication the organization can receive, and top management must analyze and interpret it. Focus on the trends that deserve attention and take action on the big issues. Keep in mind that customer feedback can be simultaneously proactive and reactive, positive and negative.

- *Progress against quality objectives.* If you chose well, your quality objectives are the true indicators of organizational success or failure. That makes them very important metrics. During management review, top management will analyze and evaluate progress against objectives. Another related topic is planning to achieve objectives.

- *Process performance and product/service conformity.* How are our processes running and what indicates that our products meet requirements? This is really two different inputs rolled into one. Process performance can be reflected by audit results, which illustrates that some of these required inputs can be satisfied by the same evidence. Examples of product conformity include inspection results, field failures, service success rate, errors discovered, and products requiring rework.

- *Nonconformities and corrective actions.* Corrective action is the formal process for solving problems and eliminating the causes of nonconformities. This process is critically important and deserves top management's careful scrutiny. Typical information presented during management review includes how many actions have been opened, how many actions have been closed, and the categories of corrective actions. Because top management has the power to motivate personnel, other good topics to consider are overdue actions and those that aren't making progress.

- *Verification results.* In subclause 9.1.1, we determined (or confirmed) the monitoring and measurement that was required. We also revisited this in subclause 9.1.3, Analysis and evaluation, which provides a direct pipeline into management review. Basically, the information and data sources that 9.1.3 requires us to analyze are a natural fit for management review and the curious eyes of top management.

- *Audit results.* This information could include positives, nonconformities, and improvement opportunities. As with all information presented to top management, strive for a concise message. Use charts and graphics whenever possible. If there have been no audits since the last management review, mention this in the records.

- *Performance of suppliers and subcontractors.* This is a topic that can easily get stuck in the weeds. Hit the high points with top management. Have we had a big failures caused by suppliers? Are our subcontractors living up to our standards? Is there anything we should do differently with managing external providers?

- *Resources.* Think about the specific resources that are important to your organization's mission. These might include tools, machines, transportation, communication, finances, people, and information. Consider these resources, especially in light of customer feedback, product conformity trends, process effectiveness, and audit results. Top management generally has the ability to acquire resources, so management review is the perfect time to evaluate whether we possess what we need to be effective.
- *Actions to address risks and opportunities.* Risks and opportunities are foundations of ISO 9001:2015. They drive some of the most significant plans that the organization can put into motion. So the question is: How effective are these plans? This is going to require that top management be familiar with the organization's risks and opportunities, and what has been implemented to address them. If risk management was done in a vacuum—without "bothering" top management—there's going to be a lot of catch up.
- *Opportunities for improvement.* Improvement is the point of management review, and some of the key inputs will be ideas and recommendations from various parts of the organization. An employee suggestion system can yield great improvement ideas. Recommendations for improvement can also be developed by key stakeholders prior to the meeting, and then proposed to top management during management review. The discussion of all the various inputs during management review will undoubtedly generate improvement opportunities.

The standard's intent is that the organization address all required inputs within the cycle defined by its management review. If the organization commits to a monthly management review, then records would indicate that all inputs were reviewed within that month-long timeframe. An effective format for management review records can be a matrix that shows the input topics in the left-hand column and the actual data discussed in the right-hand column. Because there are so many inputs that must be accounted for, make recordkeeping as systematic and error-proof as possible. Simply capturing minutes in a stream-of-consciousness manner rarely indicates that everything was addressed.

Management review outputs

ISO 9001:2015 requires that management review produce specific outputs. These outputs are actions or decisions related to three items:

- *Opportunities for improvement.* This was an input, and now it's an output. The point is that now top management will select specific opportunities to pursue. Do any products need to be improved? Do our processes require modification? Customer feedback is an especially good input for understanding what should be improved. The purview of improvement can touch almost anything in the organization.

- *Need for changes.* Based on the data presented, is there anything you need to change about your management system or your processes? Do you need any new procedures or controls? Is a new training program needed in part of your organization? Is communication effective?

- *Resource needs.* Nothing happens without resources. Because you have top management in attendance, management review is the perfect place to secure resources. Supplemented by good data and convincing messages, it should be relatively easy to secure the resources needed to drive improvement.

Just as the inputs to management review must be recorded, so must the outputs. Actions that come from management review may be recorded as corrective actions and tracked through that system. No matter how they are handled, make sure they become inputs to the next management review.

It's strongly recommended that organizations create a template or form to capture these. This will help make coverage of each required item foolproof. It could even be used as an example of error-proofing, which is required by subclause 8.5.1(g). Attempting to capture all the inputs and outputs in a free-form "memo" style of record is very difficult and nearly always results in something being left out. A form or template will prevent this problem, as it will create a visual reminder of the need for details. It's also recommended that the person facilitating management review not be the same person who creates the record. Trying to do both of these tasks usually results in neither of them being done very well.

There's a lot of redundancy within the inputs and outputs required by ISO 9001:2015. For instance, "resources" appears as both an input and an output, as does "opportunities for improvement." It's not necessary to have completely unique pieces of information to address each of these inputs and outputs. It's possible that a single discussion could cut across multiple topics. Just make a good faith attempt to address the requirements and try to use a diversity of data and information. You will most likely have some duplicate information, though, and there's nothing wrong with that.

9.3 FREQUENTLY ASKED QUESTIONS

Our general manager is frequently out of town and it's very difficult to schedule management review. Can he delegate someone to attend management review on his behalf?

No. Your management review process must involve top management. Perhaps you could explore creative ways of involving the general manager in management review when he is out of town.

Does management review have to be an actual meeting, or can we have a virtual meeting via teleconference or webinar?

Management review doesn't have to be an actual meeting. As long as you cover the required inputs and outputs, you can conduct management review in any way you see fit.

We would like to address different inputs of management review in different meetings. For example, process performance and product conformity are subjects we talk about in our weekly staff meeting. Customer feedback gets addressed at our monthly roundtable. Will this approach meet ISO 9001:2015 requirements?

Yes. You can structure your management review in any way that makes sense to you, as long as it involves top management.

Chapter 8

ISO 9001:2015 Section 10 Improvement

10.1 GENERAL

Somewhat equivalent to clauses 8.3 and 8.5.1 in ISO 9001:2008.

This section of the standard requires that you determine and select opportunities for improvement. It almost sounds as if you're required to have improvement projects in place. In fact, that's the way you should interpret it. The scope of these improvement projects is targeted at customer requirements and customer satisfaction. This might seem limiting, but it's not. Any meaningful improvements are going to ultimately affect the customer. Choose the right improvement projects and they'll fit the bill.

Management review includes both an input and an output for opportunities for improvement, so you should already have plenty of ideas floating around. The so-called opportunities for improvement can be handled in a variety of different ways. They could be action items resulting from management review, corrective actions, actions to reduce risk, planning for the achievement of quality objectives, or actions aimed at addressing customer feedback. You could even use completely separate systems to generate improvement projects or traditional quality tools. They can be generated from almost any source, including:

- Corrective actions
- Policy revisions
- Programs for achieving objectives
- Risks and opportunities
- Action items from management review
- Six Sigma projects
- Rapid *kaizen* improvements
- 5S projects
- Cycle-time reductions
- Safety and health projects
- Reduction of environmental impacts
- Waste reduction
- Profit improvement

The list goes on and on. A narrow-minded review of some of these might result in the comment, "But these have nothing to do with the customer." Hogwash. Everything the organization does ultimately affects its customers. Just be prepared to explain how your improvement also has a positive effect on your customers.

The format and methods for improvement aren't specified by ISO 9001:2015. Basically, the standard just says "Get it done." The method is up to you. A smart and efficient person is probably going to use existing processes to facilitate improvement instead of inventing processes from scratch. My personal favorite way to drive improvement is by using the corrective action system. It's simple, already established, and has project management built right into it.

This section of ISO 9001:2015 goes on to specify some topics that should be considered for improvement. These include:

- Improving products and services
- Correcting, preventing, or reducing undesired effects
- Improving the quality management system (QMS)

These are generic enough that they could apply to almost any meaningful improvement. The stronger the connection to these items, the better. The diagram shown in figure 8.1 illustrates how clauses 9.1.1, 9.1.3, 9.3, and

10.1 can fit together to achieve an elegant improvement cycle. Simple, isn't it? Please note that the opportunities from clause 6.1, Actions to address risks and opportunities, are intended to also be key inputs for your improvement projects.

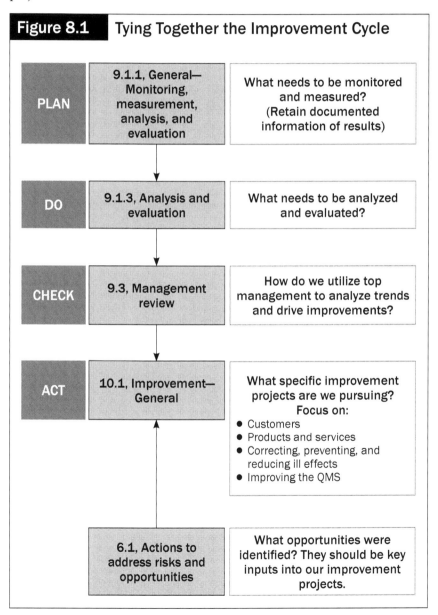

Figure 8.1 Tying Together the Improvement Cycle

| PLAN | 9.1.1, General—Monitoring, measurement, analysis, and evaluation | What needs to be monitored and measured? (Retain documented information of results) |

| DO | 9.1.3, Analysis and evaluation | What needs to be analyzed and evaluated? |

| CHECK | 9.3, Management review | How do we utilize top management to analyze trends and drive improvements? |

| ACT | 10.1, Improvement—General | What specific improvement projects are we pursuing? Focus on:
• Customers
• Products and services
• Correcting, preventing, and reducing ill effects
• Improving the QMS |

| | 6.1, Actions to address risks and opportunities | What opportunities were identified? They should be key inputs into our improvement projects. |

10.2 NONCONFORMITY AND CORRECTIVE ACTION

Equivalent to clauses 8.3 and 8.5.2 in ISO 9001:2008.

Corrective action is the process for investigating and taking action on existing problems. It's one of the most fundamental aspects of management system processes. An organization that can't solve its problems effectively is an organization that won't be in existence for very long. ISO 9001:2015 provides a set of basic steps to solve problems and attack nonconformities.

Nonconformities are the trigger for corrective actions. The title and first few words of this section make that obvious. What sorts of nonconformities might trigger corrective action? Any problem within the organization is fair game. In fact, the wider the system is applied, the better. Here are some examples of issues you could address through your corrective action system:

- Customer complaints
- Internal defects and errors
- Process inefficiencies
- Supplier problems
- Audit nonconformities
- Returned goods
- Safety incidents
- Environmental problems
- Employee ideas and feedback
- Service delays
- Cost overruns
- Failure to achieve objectives

Any activity, process, or product that doesn't meet requirements is potentially subject to corrective action. Generally, corrective action is nothing more than a system for breaking a large issue into smaller, manageable pieces. It's project management at its simplest. The project management is focused on changing the way work is done because corrective action without change is a deception.

React to the nonconformity as applicable

Nonconformities may be the trigger, but you're under no obligation to pull that trigger in every case. You decide which nonconformities require corrective action. You weigh their risks and benefits and make a rational decision for action. ISO 9001:2015 provides two possible paths to take:

- Take action to control and correct
- Deal with consequences

The decision point is the consequences, of course. You could spend every minute of every day trying to fix nonconformities and still not be finished. The good news is that not all nonconformities are created equal. Some are nuisances, others are matters of life and death. Many others exist in the great middle ground of simply not meeting a requirement. It's the organization's job to figure out where each nonconformity lies. For the nonconformities that you decide to attack, the next steps are how ISO 9001:2015 says you need to deal with them.

Review and analyze nonconformities

Before you can do anything about a nonconformity, you have to understand it. That's the point of review and analysis. You're gathering facts about the nonconformity so you can write an accurate problem statement. Are all nonconformities factually reported? Of course not. Only through exploring the nonconformity from a variety of angles will you be prepared to understand its causes. These are the questions to be answered:

- *How was the problem first reported?* This is the nonconformity, exactly as it was first reported: unfiltered and probably flawed. It will most likely focus on symptoms, but at least that's a start.
- *Who experiences the problem?* The people we identify here are usually the ones we need to interview to gain a deeper understanding of the facts related to the problem.
- *What exactly is the problem?* Here is where some preliminary investigation comes in handy. Find out what's happening beyond the raw symptoms.

- *When does the problem occur?* The timing of problems is very important. If we can pinpoint when the problem is happening, we are much closer to understanding its causes.
- *Where does the problem occur?* Most problems are localized to a specific place or set of places.
- *How often does the problem occur?* Frequency of occurrence helps clarify the scope and magnitude of a problem.

Most organizations assign each corrective action to an individual whose responsibility it is to investigate the issues surrounding the nonconformity. It's difficult to hold committees accountable, but it's easy to hold individuals accountable. The assigned person acts as the project manager for the investigation and resulting action, driving the process and recruiting other participants as necessary. The so-called project manager for a corrective action is typically the person who has the most in-depth understanding of the variables involved, although the responsibility could be assigned to anyone.

Determine the causes of the nonconformity

After defining the basic facts of nonconformity, it's time to determine causes. We must find the causes and then eliminate them. Very rarely is there a single root cause to any problem. More often, problems are caused by a chain of interrelated causes that must be identified and addressed. Organizations often do a very poor job of identifying causes. Either through ignorance or laziness, these bogus causes often appear on corrective action reports:

- Employee error
- Failure to follow procedure
- Not paying attention
- Sloppy work
- Unknown

These are bogus causes because they are all person-centered, as opposed to being process-centered. If we desire true improvement of the process, we must dig deeper to find out why the employee made the error. There was some flaw in the process that enabled the employee to make an error. We must investigate each step of the process and issues that could lead to our problem, including:

- Missing or obsolete information
- Inadequate tools
- Unclear instructions
- Flawed procedures
- Misunderstood customer requirements
- Needless complexity
- Conflicting goals
- Incompatible instructions from multiple sources
- Ineffective training

Try to identify all of a problem's existing and potential causes. In a perfect world, you would eliminate all the identified causes, but the truth is that not all causes can be removed. However, nearly all causes can be reduced. Remove or reduce all the identified causes to an acceptable level and your corrective action will have been a success.

Determine if similar nonconformities exist

ISO 9001:2015 asks you to apply broad, systematic corrective action. Don't just focus on a single nonconformity; look for similar issues in other areas of your organization. Yes, this will complicate your problem solving a bit, but it will ultimately produce more meaningful improvements. Organizations have a bad habit of taking the narrowest view possible to corrective actions. This new requirement from ISO 9001:2015 eliminates that option.

Implement actions

Once you have determined the causes of the nonconformity, the next step is action. Decide which actions are necessary to remove or reduce the causes of the problem, then make sure that the actions get implemented. This is the project management aspect of corrective action. Keep in mind that some fixes are actually a combination of many smaller fixes. Manage the process with persistence and discipline.

The plan for corrective action on a nonconformity will typically include these elements:

- *Action.* What exactly must be done? The action should be spelled out in simple terms that can be verified. Innuendo and vagueness are our enemies; we must be as specific as possible to guide those people charged with taking action. Keep in mind that this may be multiple actions.

- *Responsibility.* Who is responsible for taking action? Make sure one person is responsible, not a committee or team. The responsible person can assemble a team or committee, but we need the accountability of one responsible person. As W. Edwards Deming famously said, "Shared responsibility means nobody is responsible." Responsibility doesn't equate to being the culprit, of course.

- *Resources.* What tools, equipment, supplies, personnel, or capital are necessary to perform the actions? Don't assume that resources will magically appear. They only appear because someone made them available. By defining the necessary resources, we must decide who will provide the resources. In fact, for actions that are resource intensive, we should define exactly where the resources will come from.

- *Due date.* When exactly do we expect the action to be completed? This date is typically defined by whoever takes the action, as this person will be the best prepared to know when the action can be completed. If the due date isn't clearly defined and agreed to by all stakeholders, there's a strong chance that the action will never be completed. It may be necessary to define multiple due dates to drive incremental progress.

Review effectiveness

Reviewing effectiveness is one of the final steps for a corrective action; it's also one of the most important steps. Who should be tasked with verifying actions? People who can verify actions must fulfill two basic criteria: They need to have enough independence to review the actions in an objective manner and they must have a basic technical understanding of the issues underlying the actions. This doesn't mean that the person verifying the action has to be an expert; it only means that he or she must be able to grasp the technical effects of the action. If we're dealing with a document control problem, the technical aspects will probably be relatively minor. If we're talking about retrofitting an extruder screw to improve the plasticity of a synthetic polymer, the technical aspects might be more complicated. Use common sense.

Once it's determined who will be verifying the actions, what should verification prove? There should be at least three types of evidence:

- Evidence that the action relates to the identified root cause
- Evidence that the proposed action was actually implemented
- Evidence that the action was effective in preventing recurrence of the problem. This, clearly, is the most important detail to verify. Typically, this type of evidence might take some time to compile, requiring that actions remain open longer than expected. It's better that actions remain open and ultimately lead to true prevention of recurrence than be closed in a hurry and achieve only nice, clean records.

Update risks and opportunities

Way back in clause 6.1, we determined risks, opportunities, and the actions to address them. Risks and opportunities are dynamic processes, always subject to change. If you're using your corrective action system correctly, the overall risks to your organization will be decreased. That's ultimately what a corrective action system is: a risk reduction strategy. Yes, most corrective actions are triggered by existing nonconformities, which means the risks have already born fruit. Long-term risk is reduced, though, because we've removed or reduced the problem causes. With mitigation of problem causes, the overall composition of our risk portfolio is altered. An effective corrective action will always reduce the overall risk to the organization. The primary reason that ISO 9001:2015 asks you to "determine if similar nonconformities exist" is so you can lower overall risk by applying corrective action.

When your organization closes a corrective action, make sure to revisit your risk planning. Appropriately modify any ratings for the risk that has been addressed. If the nonconformity revealed a risk that hadn't even been identified, make sure to add it to your risk portfolio.

Make changes to the QMS

Changing the QMS is the primary way that you sustain the improvements made by corrective actions. Improvements, without a mechanism to make them permanent, are almost worthless. Organizational inertia will quickly move things back to their original place. When you make improvements through a corrective action, consider the following changes to your QMS:

- Revise existing procedures.
- Develop new documentation.
- Establish new recordkeeping.
- Establish new monitoring and measurement.
- Revise existing training materials.
- Add to your communication plan and/or awareness program.
- Revise roles, responsibilities, and authorities.
- Enhance your company's organizational knowledge.
- Revise purchasing contracts.
- Revisit your change management process.

Not all of these will be appropriate. However, at least one or two of them always apply. Carefully examine which parts of your QMS can assist in sustaining change and improvement. Remember: The most brilliant improvement is nothing more than tomfoolery if it's not sustained.

Corrective actions appropriate to the effects

ISO 9001:2015 also tells us that corrective action must be appropriate to the effects of the nonconformities encountered. This means that big problems get big solutions and little problems get little solutions. It gives us the discretion of applying appropriate fixes. Sometimes, we decide not to apply a fix because the effect of the nonconformity is negligible. This isn't a loophole to allow organizations to avoid facing their problems. It simply allows you to direct your resources where they're most needed. You could do nothing but solve problems 24 hours a day, but not all problems are created equal. Attack the ones that have the most bearing on your success and follow through all the way to completion.

Retain documented information

Corrective actions are an important part of an organization's history. As such, you will need to retain documented information (i.e., keep records) on all aspects of your corrective action process. ISO 9001:2015 does require records and is precise about its requirements:

- *Records of the nature of the nonconformities.* In other words, a description or problem statement. Describe the problem factually and try to define the requirement or standard that it violates.

- *Records of actions taken.* These are what you do to reduce or remove the causes of nonconformities. Small corrective actions can be described in a couple of sentences. More complex ones may require a full project plan.

- *Records of the results of corrective action.* What did the action achieve? Does evidence indicate that the causes have been removed or reduced? If evidence doesn't indicate that the causes of the problem have been removed or reduced, then the actions didn't achieve their objectives. Send it back for rework.

10.2 FREQUENTLY ASKED QUESTIONS

We have a separate procedure for each type of corrective action. We have one for supplier corrective actions, one for audit corrective actions, and another for customer complaints. Is this OK?

Yes. Structure your corrective action process in whatever way makes the most sense to you.

Some of our corrective actions have been open for over half a year because they involve capital investments. Is it OK for them to remain open so long?

Yes. As long as you're making progress on the actions and updating the records, there's no problem at all.

10.3 CONTINUAL IMPROVEMENT

Equivalent to subclause 8.5.1 in ISO 9001:2008.

Continual improvement is the process of becoming a more effective organization. It's an incremental process, meaning you'll take many small steps toward improvement. Huge breakthroughs would be nice, but the reality of business is that there are only so many big wins out there. The trick is to put processes in place that will drive improvement across a wide swath of your organization and involve as many people as possible.

ISO 9001:2015 requires continual improvement of the QMS. Any organization in business should have no trouble finding some evidence of improvement within its operation. If you're using the prescribed tools, continual improvement will become almost automatic. In fact, this clause is more philosophical than practical. We have already discussed a variety of ISO 9001:2015's requirements for taking action on improvement opportunities. These appeared in clauses 6.1.2, Actions to address risks and opportunities; 6.2, Quality objectives and planning to achieve them; 6.3, Planning of changes; 9.2, Internal audit; 10.2, Nonconformity and corrective action; and 9.3, Management review. Could some of these be considered "continual improvement"? Of course. If you've already implemented ISO 9001:2015, it's unlikely that you're going to need to do anything special to address 10.3, Continual improvement, because you've already created continual improvement. It's here as a reminder, just in case something slipped through the cracks of your QMS.

This requirement asks you to examine the results of these two processes to see if there are new opportunities for continual improvement:

- *Analysis and evaluation (9.1.3).* Data and information can reveal opportunities, threats, risks, and untold other issues. The trick is to make analysis and evaluation systematic: a transparent part of the way you do business. Conversion of data into graphics and simple statistics can facilitate its interpretation and analysis. As we mentioned earlier, management review can serve as a convenient forum for analyzing data and making decisions based on the analysis.
- *Management review (9.3).* This is where top management reviews the organization's results and the output of the management system to de-

termine where further improvements can be made. It's one of the most important processes in the entire management system. Far from being a "dog and pony show," the intent is to truly analyze trends and data and decide what actions should be taken to drive the organization forward.

Although you are required to continually improve the QMS, you're also strongly encouraged to improve the overall performance of your organization. In fact, there's little point in improving the management system if it doesn't in turn improve the organization's overall performance, efficiency, and effectiveness. Strive for the higher standard of improvement and you'll be sure to at least hit the mark required by ISO 9001:2015.

10.3 FREQUENTLY ASKED QUESTIONS

Do we need to establish a stand-alone continual improvement program?

No, there is no need to establish a stand-alone continual improvement program. As long as you're using your other improvement processes correctly (quality objectives, internal audits, analysis and evaluation, corrective actions, and management review), then together they constitute your continual improvement process.

Can we use our lean enterprise program to satisfy the continual improvement requirements of ISO 9001:2015?

Yes, of course. Use whatever tools and processes work best in your unique situation.

Chapter 9

Conclusion: Implementing ISO 9001:2015

Y ou made it to the end of the book! Congratulations on your endurance in the face of such a daunting task. I hope you found the material helpful. You may wonder the order in which you should implement the requirements of the standard. There are countless ways that an organization could implement ISO 9001:2015, but the following sequence will get you started. Make sure to prioritize your implementation steps based on your needs and circumstances. The purpose of this isn't to be prescriptive, but to get your wheels rolling as you develop your own implementation plan.

And just another reminder here: This book is not intended as a replacement for the ISO 9001:2015 standard. If you haven't read the standard, do so—now! It's also a good idea to read ISO 9000:2015, which is the normative reference for ISO 9001:2015. You can buy them both through *www.iso.org.*

STEP 1: UNDERSTANDING THE ORGANIZATION AND ITS CONTEXT (CLAUSE 4.1)

The first step to doing anything successfully is understanding what you're working with. Understand your organization: its strengths and weaknesses, values, and beliefs. Then take a look around you at the environment that forms the context of your organization. Depending on the size and type of company this context could be a neighborhood or the entire world. Perform this examination as objectively as possible. The results will be key inputs to a number of other sections of ISO 9001:2015.

STEP 2: UNDERSTANDING THE NEEDS AND EXPECTATIONS OF INTERESTED PARTIES (CLAUSE 4.2)

This requirement proceeds logically from clause 4.1. It's exploratory in nature, asking the organization to take an inventory of its stakeholders. Many organizations don't seem to even understand their customers, let alone interested parties such as employees, suppliers, regulators, and neighbors. An understanding of interested parties is a natural extension of the organization's context. Armed with clear-eyed knowledge from clauses 4.1 and 4.2, the organization has a solid base on which to build its quality management system (QMS).

STEP 3: DETERMINING THE SCOPE OF THE QMS (CLAUSE 4.3)

It's either luck or genius that the first three sections of ISO 9001:2015 are also the first that organizations should implement. Either way, it's time to draw the boundary around your QMS. Smart companies will utilize their QMS as broadly as possible. The biggest issues identified in clauses 4.1 and 4.2 should certainly fall within the QMS scope. If you can't manage the big issues, what's the point of having a QMS?

STEP 4: ORGANIZATIONAL ROLES, RESPONSIBILITIES, AND AUTHORITIES (CLAUSE 5.3)

Now that we've laid some ground work with the QMS, we need establish its basic roles, responsibilities, and authorities. In addition to the roles specifically mentioned in clause 5.3, you might want to consider establishing an ISO 9001 steering committee. This is a leadership group that would oversee the implementation of ISO 9001:2015, provide direction, and remove obstacles. Another entity that many organizations benefit from is an ISO 9001 work group. This is a team of hands-on personnel who report to the ISO 9001 steering committee.

STEP 5: DEVELOP AND COMMUNICATE THE QUALITY POLICY (CLAUSE 5.2)

If you don't already have a quality policy, you need to work with top management to write one. If you already have a policy, verify that it's aligned with your organizational context and overall strategy. The age of generic quality policies is over. Your quality policy needs to be specific to your organization and be the top-level document for your entire system. Employees need to be able to read the quality policy and agree, "Yes, that's us."

STEP 6: ADDRESS RISKS AND OPPORTUNITIES (CLAUSE 6.1)

As you've heard countless times by now, ISO 9001:2015 is a risk-based standard. It would have been meaningless to try to identify risks and opportunities before implementing earlier requirements of ISO 9001:2015. Now you should be well-armed. Remind yourself of what you learned in clauses 4.1 and 4.2 and brainstorm all the risks and opportunities within the scope of the QMS. Then match the risks and opportunities with actions that will minimize risks and maximize opportunities. Make sure that top management and other influential personnel are involved in this, as the work you do here will influence many other sections of ISO 9001:2015.

STEP 7: QUALITY OBJECTIVES AND ACTIONS TO ACHIEVE THEM (CLAUSE 6.2)

Your quality objectives will be the guiding lights of your QMS. The quality policy will provide general guidance to develop quality objectives. Specific guidance will be provided by risks and opportunities and the overall strategy of the organization. Remember that quality objectives must be matched with project plans. After establishing the quality policy, quality objectives, and risks and opportunities, you can make your personnel aware of them.

STEP 8: LEADERSHIP AND COMMITMENT—GENERAL (SUBCLAUSE 5.1.1)

By now, there will be an awareness within the organization that things are changing. ISO 9001:2015 creates new processes. Top management must manage this effort and make sure everybody understands its importance. The QMS will be a frequent topic of communication, and employees will play a direct leadership role in the implementation effort.

STEP 9: AWARENESS AND COMMUNICATION (CLAUSES 7.3 AND 7.4)

Awareness and communication are siblings within the ISO 9001:2015 framework. Awareness is prescriptive; it defines what you need to make employees aware of. Communication leaves it up to the organization. Both processes have the objective of sharing information. Your QMS is already producing important information, so it should be a relatively simple matter of building a plan to pass this information along to those who need it. Early in the ISO 9001:2015 implementation process, it's impossible to communicate too much.

STEP 10: QMS AND ITS PROCESSES (CLAUSE 4.4)

Some high-level process control is now needed. Identify the processes of the QMS and order them as related activities linked through a common goal. Make sure to determine all the various elements of each process, such as inputs, outputs, criteria, methods, and resources. Documenting these processes creates an excellent introduction to your QMS that can be used as a training and process control tool. Clause 4.4 (along with clause 4.3) are the remnants of what used to be the quality manual in previous versions of ISO 9001.

STEP 11: DOCUMENTED INFORMATION (CLAUSE 7.5)

Despite the fact that ISO 9001:2015 seems to de-emphasize the role of documentation, it's still a hallmark of any effective QMS; anything less is tribal knowledge. If you don't already have a functioning system for document control, now is the time to establish one. Because a great deal of what you create when you implement a QMS is a document of some sort, you need a way to control it all. Record control will also be necessary but early in the process document control is usually more important.

STEP 12: RESOURCES (CLAUSES 7.1, 7.1.1, 7.1.2, 7.1.3, AND 7.1.4)

It makes sense to tackle these resource elements at the same time. Subclauses 7.1.1, General, and 7.1.2, People, do nothing more than check that you have the correct resources in place. Subclause 7.1.3, Infrastructure, has more meat to it, as an organization will usually need to verify that it has the proper infrastructure in place and that maintenance activities are established and completed. Subclause 7.1.4, Environment, is very similar. Depending on the type of product or service being provided, environment could be a complicated consideration, requiring a great deal of monitoring and control.

STEP 13: REQUIREMENTS FOR PRODUCTS AND SERVICES (CLAUSE 8.2)

Customers are the reason your organization exists. This element requires that you establish communication processes with customers, and processes for capturing product and service requirements. You must also ensure that product and service requirements are systematically reviewed. If your organization is already in business, you probably have at least some of these activities already in place. Ensure that all components of clause 8.2 are in place. Products and services delivered to the wrong specifications are a common and costly mistake.

STEP 14: CONTROL OF PRODUCTION AND SERVICE PROVISION (SUBCLAUSE 8.5.1)

One of the most important things that a QMS can do is help you produce products or services more effectively. Depending on the size of your operation, this could consist of dozens activities and tasks. The controlled conditions shown in items a–h of this subclause are obvious concerns, but another significant item isn't even mentioned in ISO 9001:2015: the development of work instructions. Simple, concise, and graphic work instructions are one of the most useful tools you have for controlling your production processes. Brainstorm processes that would benefit from work instructions, build a project plan for their development, and start writing. Other processes that are closely related to subclause 8.5.1—and which are often addressed at the same time—include:

- 8.5.2 —Identification and traceability
- 8.5.3—Property belonging to customers or external providers
- 8.5.4—Preservation
- 8.5.5—Post-delivery activities

STEP 15: DESIGN AND DEVELOPMENT (CLAUSE 8.3)

Design and development doesn't apply to all organizations, but for those for whom it does, it's significant. It's also a process that has a long learning curve. Build the various processes of design (planning, inputs, controls, outputs, and changes), and make sure they link together as seamlessly as possible.

STEP 16: MONITORING AND MEASURING RESOURCES (SUBCLAUSE 7.1.5)

For organizations that utilize measuring devices, demonstrating fitness for purpose usually represents a significant dedication of time and effort. What should be calibrated and/or verified? How often should it happen? Who should perform the work? What records will be maintained? All these questions must be answered and matched with supporting activities.

STEP 17: **RELEASE OF PRODUCTS AND SERVICES (CLAUSE 8.6)**

Another very practical requirement to tackle at this point is release of products and services. These are the inspection, test, and verification activities that ensure your products and services meet all requirements. It's one of the most fundamental quality control activities and one that delivers immediate value. Try to perform the "release" of products as quickly after production as possible.

STEP 18: **CONTROL OF NONCONFORMING OUTPUTS (CLAUSE 8.7)**

Any time inspection, test, and verification activities take place, there's the chance that something may not meet requirements. This is where control of nonconforming outputs comes in. It's one of the most basic quality control activities and something that even companies with well-established QMSs struggle with.

STEP 19: **NONCONFORMITY AND CORRECTIVE ACTION (CLAUSE 10.2)**

Your corrective action process is the way you deal with nonconformities that pose a significant risk to your success. Does that sound important? Yes. It's also a process that doesn't come naturally to most organizations. Corrective action is structured problem solving that can potentially be triggered by virtually any other process in ISO 9001:2015.

STEP 20: **CONTROL OF EXTERNALLY PROVIDED PROCESSES, PRODUCTS, AND SERVICES (CLAUSE 8.4)**

Your external providers are key partners in your success. If you choose providers that lack capabilities or resources, you will suffer. You will also suffer if you fail to communicate with your suppliers. Build a process for proactively managing your external providers and make sure it's understood by everyone involved.

STEP 21: **PLAN AND CONTROL CHANGES (CLAUSES 6.3 AND 8.5.6)**

Change management is one of the key themes of ISO 9001:2015. The point is not to react to change, but to understand it, plan it, and manage change so it produces effective results. Establish processes for managing change and make sure that supervisors are comfortable leading the effort. If your front-line leaders don't see value in change management, it will die before it even gets off the ground.

STEP 22: **COMPETENCE (CLAUSE 7.2)**

It seems like we've waited a long time to talk about competence and training. This is because early in the implementation process, you're not entirely sure what constitutes competency. After all, the processes and controls of the QMS are still being developed. By now, we should know what our people need to be effective. Define the competency requirements for each category of employee, close the competency gaps, and make sure to maintain records.

STEP 23: **ORGANIZATIONAL KNOWLEDGE (SUBCLAUSE 7.1.6)**

Is your company learning anything yet? I sure hope so. You're probably experiencing all sorts of lessons. Let's establish a process so that we don't forget what we're learning. The method for maintaining organizational knowledge will probably be related to the method for maintaining documented information, so make sure to leverage your existing processes.

STEP 24: MONITORING, MEASUREMENT, ANALYSIS, AND EVALUATION (SUBCLAUSES 9.1.1 AND 9.1.3)

You and your team have established a great many processes. Now you need to monitor, measure, analyze, and evaluate them. Subclause 9.1.1 asks you to determine what needs to be monitored and measured. Subclause 9.1.3 asks you analyze and evaluate certain types of data. They go hand in hand to provide the information that flows into management review and which ultimately provides the raw material for continual improvement.

STEP 25: CUSTOMER SATISFACTION (SUBCLAUSE 9.1.2)

One of the most important sources of information you can capture is customer feedback. At this point in the implementation, you have enough process discipline and improvement tools to effectively take action on the feedback. Utilize existing interactions with your customers to capture feedback on a continual basis and you will always have your finger on your customers' pulse.

STEP 26: MANAGEMENT REVIEW (CLAUSE 9.3)

In many ways, management review is the most important process in the entire QMS. It represents top management doing its job: leading the organization and managing for success. You could have implemented management review much earlier in the effort, but you didn't have all the required inputs. Now you do. If you already have meetings in which organizational performance is assessed (such as monthly financial review), they may also be utilized for management review. Keep in mind that management review can be a combination of different meetings, and it doesn't even have to be a meeting.

STEP 27: GENERAL IMPROVEMENT/CONTINUAL IMPROVEMENT (CLAUSES 10.1 AND 10.3)

Management review will reveal improvement opportunities, as will many other interactions that involve information and decision makers. These opportunities will become projects with the ultimate result of continual improvement. The improvements might be small—and may occasionally be a step backward—but the overall momentum is always toward a more successful organization.

STEP 28: INTERNAL AUDIT (CLAUSE 9.2)

Auditing is another process that actually could have been implemented much earlier, at least in part. Many practitioners recommend beginning internal auditing soon after processes are established and producing results. This is actually a good idea. My placement of auditing as the very last process simply reflects the fact that you can't perform a full cycle of audits until everything else in the QMS is in place.

IN CONCLUSION

These are the major implementation steps in ISO 9001:2015, although not every element in the standard. Some requirements, such as subclause 5.1.2, Customer focus, are achieved by doing other things in the QMS. You wouldn't necessarily have to attack the requirement directly, because it makes more sense to address it through related processes. Remember that your own implementation plan might be quite a bit different from what I have proposed. However, I feel confident in saying that the first ten steps would work in nearly any organization. So, what are you waiting for? Let's implement ISO 9001:2015! Thank you for choosing this book to assist in your efforts.

Additional Requirements Beyond ISO 9001:2008

A s a convenience to those who already have a certified quality management system (QMS) in place, here are the ISO 9001:2015 requirements that go beyond ISO 9001:2008's requirements.

Clause No.	Title	Explanation
4.1	Understanding the organization and its context	Completely new requirement. This clause represents a step toward strategic planning and a broadening of the influence of the QMS.
4.2	Understanding the needs and expectations of interested parties	Completely new requirement. This clause and the previous one work together intellectually.
4.3	Determining the scope of the QMS	Partially new. A documented QMS scope has always been a requirement, but now you must consider the outputs of 4.1 and 4.2. Also the scope must include the products and services covered.
4.4	QMS and its processes	Slightly new. The process requirements here are very similar to what was addressed in clause 4.1 of ISO 9001:2008. The difference is that ISO 9001:2015 provides more detail on what it considers a process.

Clause No.	Title	Explanation
5.1.1	Leadership and commitment—General	Added commitments that top management must demonstrate: taking account of the effectiveness of the QMS and ensuring integration of the QMS into the organization's business processes.
5.1.2(b)	Customer focus	Added a requirement that risks and opportunities affecting customer satisfaction must be addressed.
5.2.1(a)	Establishing the quality policy	Added a requirement that the quality policy must support the strategic direction of the organization.
5.2.2(c)	Communicating the quality policy	Added a requirement that the quality policy must be available to applicable interested parties.
5.3(b)	Organizational roles, responsibilities, and authorities	Additional role: ensuring that processes deliver intended outputs
6.1	Actions to address risks and opportunities	Completely new requirement. This clause borrows themes from ISO 9001:2008 subclauses 8.5.3, Preventive action, and 5.4.2, Quality management system planning.
6.2.2	Quality objectives and planning to achieve them	Added a requirement for plans for achieving quality objectives: what needs to be done, what resources are needed, who is responsible, when it needs to be completed, and how results are evaluated.
6.3	Planning of changes	Partially new. Somewhat equivalent to subclause 5.4.2 of ISO 9001:2008, but with many additional requirements. A number of considerations must be made prior to initiating change. See 6.3 (a–d).
7.1.5	Monitoring and measuring resources	Very similar to clause 7.6 in ISO 9001:2008, but "fitness for purpose" is the new focus.
7.1.6	Organizational knowledge	Completely new requirement.
7.3	Awareness	Added requirements for being aware of the benefits of improved performance and implications of nonconformance with the QMS.

Clause No.	Title	Explanation
7.4	Communication	Added requirements for planning of communications: what, when, to whom, how, and by whom?
8.4.2(c) (2)	Type and extent of control	Added a requirement for taking into consideration controls applied by external providers.
8.5.3	Property belonging to customers or external providers	Added a requirement for controlling property belonging to external providers.
8.5.5	Post-delivery activities	Added considerations for determining post-delivery activities. See 8.5.5 (a–e).
8.5.6	Control of changes	Added requirements for reviewing changes, keeping records of the results of changes, and necessary actions arising from the review. Similar to requirements in subclauses 4.2.3 and 5.4.2 in ISO 9001:2008.
9.1.1	Monitoring, measurement, analysis, and evaluation—General	Added requirement for keeping records. Otherwise equivalent to clause 8.1 in ISO 9001:2008.
9.1.3	Analysis and evaluation	Added requirement for evaluating effectiveness of actions on risks and opportunities, and if planning has been effectively implemented. Otherwise equivalent to clause 8.4 in ISO 9001:2008.
9.3	Management review	Added requirements for the following inputs: changes in external and internal issues; extent to which quality objectives have been met; performance of external providers; and effectiveness of actions on risks and opportunities.
10.1	Improvement—General	Added requirement for determining and selecting opportunities for improvement. Otherwise equivalent to clauses 8.3 and 8.5.1 in ISO 9001:2008.
10.2.1(b) (3)	Nonconformity and corrective action	Added requirement for determining if similar nonconformities exist or potentially could occur.

Validation of Processes When Output Cannot Be Verified

Validation is the method used to ensure that the outputs of a process are highly predictable. Through a mix of review, control, monitoring, and qualification, we can almost guarantee that a process will produce conforming products. ISO 9001:2015 requires that you validate processes whose products fall into two categories:

- Products that can't be verified, either because the technology doesn't exist or is too expensive
- Products whose defects only become apparent after the product is in use

In these cases, you really want a process you can rely on. That's the point of validation: to create a process that's so consistent that you know exactly what it will produce.

DESTRUCTIVE TESTING

In theory, destructive testing can reveal a great deal about the conformity of the product. Due to its very nature, it's expensive and only representative of a small fraction of process output. Processes that produce products that are only verifiable through destructive testing must be validated.

EXAMPLES OF PROCESSES THAT MIGHT REQUIRE VALIDATION

There are no hard and fast answers for which processes require validation. In general, the following processes are candidates for validation because their products can't be verified, are too expensive to verify, or their defects only become known after use:

- Welding
- Brazing and soldering
- Sterilization
- Purification
- Protective coatings and surface treatment
- Plating and anodizing
- Flame spraying
- Shot peening
- Heat treating
- Software used to perform calculations or make decisions
- Aseptic filling
- Retort food canning
- Preparation and serving of foods that are potentially dangerous
- Manufacturing of implantable medical devices
- Load-bearing construction
- Tunnel grouting
- Concrete compaction
- Medical decisions
- Assembly of automobile air bags
- Bomb assembly
- Processes used in the execution of criminals

VALIDATION SHALL DEMONSTRATE THE ABILITY OF PROCESSES

ISO 9001:2015 doesn't provide much guidance for performing process validation. Those decisions are left up to you. The standard simply says that validation must demonstrate the ability of processes to achieve planned results. In theory, it would be a good idea to validate all processes prior to beginning production. However, validation can be an expensive and time-consuming activity. Some aspects of validation can certainly be applied as the organization sees fit, even when the processes concerned produce verifiable products.

DEFINED CRITERIA FOR REVIEW AND APPROVAL OF THE PROCESSES

Here are some typical criteria for review and approval of a process:

- *Determination of key process parameters.* What parameters are critically important in operating the process? This will differ widely depending on the nature of the process. Some key process parameters that might apply include temperature, humidity, time, pressure, speed, vibration, purity, cleanliness, and many others.

- *Establishment of process control limits.* What are the statistical limits that indicate the inherent stability of a process? Process control limits are often applied to the key process parameters.

- *Potential failure modes.* What could possibly fail with the process, and how likely is each failure? What should be done to prevent the failures? What should be done as a corrective measure if the failure happens anyway?

- *Raw material requirements.* What raw materials must be used for the process to operate effectively? What are the tolerances and specifications for the raw materials? What suppliers should be used to purchase raw materials?

APPROVAL OF EQUIPMENT AND QUALIFICATION OF PERSONNEL

This clause actually mentions two different issues: equipment and personnel. Let's address one at a time. Equipment is the infrastructure that enables the process to function. It can include machinery, tools, molds, jigs, ovens, computers, and other equipment. You must establish the requirements around equipment. In other words, what should you verify about equipment that will enable you to have confidence in its output?

Here are some examples:

- *Equipment design.* How should the equipment be designed and constructed? What materials should be used? What special features are necessary?
- *Calibration.* If the equipment takes measurements, then ensuring those measurements are accurate is very important.
- *Maintenance.* Beyond calibration, what sort of cleaning, lubrication, tuning, and checking is necessary to keep the equipment working? How often should these maintenance steps be carried out?
- *Spare parts.* What parts should be kept on hand in the event of breakdown? What is the appropriate quantity of parts? Are there special preservation requirements related to spare parts, and can we perform the preservation?
- *Equipment manuals and troubleshooting guides.* What documentation do we need to have on-hand to effectively operate the process? Who will be responsible for ensuring we have the most current revision of documentation? (Keep in mind that this is external documentation, and you're usually relying on publications from equipment manufacturers.)
- *Environmental conditions.* What environmental conditions are necessary for the equipment to function properly? Do you have the ability to maintain the required environmental conditions?

Qualification of personnel will address all the necessary attributes of people controlling the process. The issues addressed here will be very similar to the competency requirements described in clause 7.2:

- *Training requirements.* What training is required to operate the process? Who will provide the training, and what will indicate effectiveness? What will trigger retraining?
- *Education requirements.* Do personnel require any special education, certificates, or degrees?
- *Skill requirements.* Do personnel need to possess specific skills to effectively control the process? How will skills be verified? Should skills be periodically reverified?
- *Experience requirements.* Are there experience requirements for personnel controlling or operating the process?

USE OF SPECIFIC METHODS AND PROCEDURES

Obviously, a process whose outputs can't be verified must have some specific methods and procedures. ISO 9001:2015 doesn't explicitly require that these procedures be documented, but it would be difficult to communicate them consistently otherwise. Here are some typical methods, procedures, and documents that might be considered:

- Start-up checklists
- Standard operating procedures
- Raw material specifications
- Troubleshooting guides
- Flow diagrams of the overall process
- Emergency procedures
- Shutdown procedures
- Maintenance checklists
- Calibration procedures

REQUIREMENTS FOR RECORDS

It would be difficult to prove validation was performed without records. Even though ISO 9001:2015 doesn't explicitly require records here, you should define exactly what records will be maintained as part of process validation. These activities related to process validation will nearly always produce records worth maintaining: determination of key process parameters, failure mode and effects analysis, supplier qualification results, equipment design, training and competency of personnel, maintenance, calibration, environmental monitoring, and process changes.

REVALIDATION

Revalidation requires that you go through the whole process from the start. Because validation can be expensive and time-consuming, you want to have a good reason for doing this. Here are some of the most common reasons for revalidating a process:

- Changes in product requirements
- Changes in key process parameters
- Shifting production to a new facility
- Environmental changes
- Changes in raw materials
- Purchase of new equipment

Work Instructions

Work instructions aren't even mentioned in ISO 9001:2015. Nonetheless, there are few quality management system (QMS) tools that are simpler or more effective. Work instructions also fit right into the new requirement for preventing human error (8.5.1(g)). For these reasons, I thought it would be helpful to provide a brief appendix on the topic.

Work instructions are a type of procedure. The content is usually very specific, defining individual tasks and job steps. They can take many different forms: flowcharts, checklists, text procedures, diagrams, photographs, and drawings. Anything that provides procedural information at a task level might be considered a work instruction. Here are some criteria that might help you decide if work instructions are necessary:

- *Infrequent tasks.* If a job is performed very infrequently, it's possible that personnel may need work instructions.
- *Important tasks.* If a job is very important or high risk, it may need to be defined in a work instruction. Checklists can be an effective type of work instruction in these cases, especially when there are multiple steps that must be performed.
- *Complicated tasks.* If a job requires complicated tasks or many different process steps, a work instruction might be necessary.

Identifying the need for working instructions is fairly simple. Brainstorm a list of the tasks and activities in each department. Then ask the following questions about each task or activity. If you answer "yes" to any of these, seriously consider documenting the task in a simple and concise way.

- Employees find the task confusing.
- It's important that this task be performed consistently.
- We have to inspect the output of this task.
- This task could not be performed correctly by a novice.
- Supervisors have to oversee this task.
- We have experienced errors and defects with this task.
- This task includes multiple steps or decisions.
- I would feel more confident as a supervisor if this task was documented.
- Mistakes at this task are expensive or time-consuming to fix.
- Specialized training is required for this task.

When documenting production tasks, try to limit the procedure to one page. Keep in mind that the most effective documentation is usually posted directly at the work station.

Index